PARENT POWER

Operation Maths

Matador
9 Priory Business Park,
Wistow Road, Kibworth Beauchamp,
Leicestershire. LE8 0RX
Tel: 0116 279 2299
Email: books@troubador.co.uk
Web: www.troubador.co.uk/matador
Twitter: @matadorbooks

ISBN 978 1838591 212

British Library Cataloguing in Publication Data.
A catalogue record for this book is available from the British Library.

Printed and bound by CPI Group (UK) Ltd, Croydon, CR0 4YY

Matador is an imprint of Troubador Publishing Ltd

Contents

Introduction

Maths is fun, although not everybody thinks so. Some children take to maths quite easily, but not all and even those children who usually enjoy maths can sometimes get stuck. The aim of this book is to empower parents to support their children in learning the arithmetic that underpins maths at primary school and beyond. It is not only for parents who struggle with maths, but also for those who don't know the methods taught in primary schools today, and so find it difficult to help their children with their maths homework.

The book describes how addition, subtraction, multiplication and division are taught from the beginning of primary school to when children leave aged eleven. It explains the progression of coherent techniques that take the child from first steps to a solid understanding of each operation and shows that the most appropiate method to use to solve a particular problem is not always the last one that has been learnt.

Everybody can do maths given the right teaching and enough time to learn. In discussions with parents about their children's learning I am often told, with the child listening: "Well I wasn't any good at maths, so I know where they get it from." It is no surprise then that these children believe that it is 'alright' for them to not be able to do maths or even to think that they are not capable, just like their parents.

Using this book, you will discover that you can do maths and you can help your child.

The power of confidence

Believing in yourself and your abilities has a huge impact on the way you approach tasks. If you believe that you are going to succeed you are open to new ideas, you allow yourself to absorb new information and, crucially, you are not put off when you make mistakes. In fact, realising why you've made mistakes leads to a deeper understanding. In contrast, if you decide that you are 'no good' at something you shut off the ability to think clearly and often cannot process the new concepts that you are being taught. Mistakes, instead of leading to learning, just seem to reinforce your negative view of the subject. Remember, the person who has never made a mistake has never done anything!

What we need for our children is the openness and freedom that confidence brings them to take on new ideas. Not everyone learns at the same speed, or in fact in the same way, but that does not matter as long as their learning is always moving forward. The most important way you can help your children with their progress in maths is not by teaching them their times tables or how to do long division, although these are very useful, but is to encourage them to have the confidence to give maths a go.

To prevent confidence being eroded it is vital that children learn at their own pace and do not move on to the next stage until the current one is secure. There is often a perceived pressure to 'keep up' with others, which can have a damaging effect on children and their enjoyment of the subject. With maths in particular, a solid understanding of the basic principles is more important than an incomplete understanding of a wider range of concepts. Throughout a child's mathematics learning, ideas are revisited and built on many times. Shortcutting the foundations will only lead to difficulties in understanding later on.

How to use the book

The book is organised into four main chapters; one for each mathematical operation - addition, subtraction, multiplication and division. Each chapter is divided into the seven stages of development used in most primary schools. These move from basic counting using real objects through to formal written methods to solve calculations with large or decimal numbers.

One way to use the book is to go through all the stages of the operation yourself first so that you are confident with the methods that schools use, before returning to the stage at which your child requires help. Alternatively, you can go directly to the section with which your son or daughter needs help. In this case, be sure you understand the method thoroughly before you begin working with your child on it. To check that you understand the method, I suggest that you always read the introduction to the chapter so that you are familiar with the fundamental concepts of the operation and then skim through all the stages up to the one on which you want to focus.

To help understand the maths vocabulary used in schools there are pink vocabulary boxes to explain the terms, as well as ParentPower hints and tips.

At the end of each stage are a few activities that I would encourage you to do with your child at home. All of these activities support work at the current stage, or are good preparation for the next one. They concentrate on mental maths activities that underpin the written methods and, although covered in school, your child will always benefit from more time spent on them at home.

Helping your child to succeed

In order to get the most from the book my suggestions are:

1   Decide that maths is fun and that you and your child are going to explore it together.

2   Use the book to give yourself confidence with the methods used in primary arithmetic and pass on that confidence to your child.

3   Read through as many sections from the beginning of a chapter as you need to before you start helping with homework.

4   Encourage your child to have a go at as many of the activities from the 'Activities to help at home' sections as possible.

5   Look for as many real-life maths problems to solve with your child as you can.

6   Go at your child's pace. Take the lead from the work the teacher has set and let your child enjoy being good at each stage before moving on.

Addition

This chapter takes you through seven stages that lead to an understanding of **column addition**. Please note that these stages do not directly correspond to what is taught in each of the seven primary school years. Some stages will be passed through quite quickly and others will take much longer to understand fully and become confident in. For each stage a few activities are provided for you to do with your children to support them with their school work.

Is all addition the same?

We use addition for one of two reasons: we may want to put two or more quantities together (this is called aggregation) where we **count all** the numbers. For example:

> *I have 3 toy cars and 2 toy cars.*
> *How many cars have I got altogether?*

Or we we may have a quantity to start with and then want to add another quantity onto it. So we need to **count on** (this is called augmentation). For example:

> *I begin with 3 cars and add 2 more. How many cars have I got now?*

However, both of these types of addition can be recorded like this:

Pictorially   **Numerically**

   +  =   3 + 2 =

For the **count all** calculation we start from the first car and count through all the cars.

For the **count on** calculation we start from three and count two more on.

Of course, the eventual result will be the same for either calculation.

Children begin to learn addition through counting real objects.

Firstly they are given two sets of familiar objects and asked to work out how many objects they have altogether.

The children are shown how to gather the two sets of objects together and count all the items one by one (in other words they are shown how to **count all**).

Next they are given a number of objects and are asked how many they have. Then more objects are added and the children are asked how many there are now.

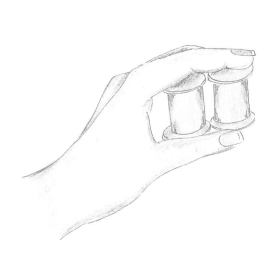 

The children are shown how to count the first set of objects and then continue to count on the number that are added (in other words they are shown how to **count on**).

1 Practise counting favourite objects up to 10, then up to 20.

2 Practise counting to 10 on fingers.

3 Practise counting objects in pictures.
   For example: *How many flowers can you see in the picture?*

4 Have two piles of toys.
   Ask: *How many toys are there altogether?*
   Encourage your child to move the toys to a new pile as they count.

5 Begin with up to 10 toys and move onto 20.

6 Give your child up to 5 toys and ask: *How many have you got?*
   Give them a few more and ask: *How many have you got now?*
   To begin with they may begin counting all the toys from the beginning again which is fine, but over time encourage them to start from the total number in the first set and count on from there.

7 When ready, move onto three sets of objects.

8 Try to use different words for adding:
   *What is 4 dolls **and** 2 dolls?*
   ***Add** 4 bricks and 6 bricks together.*
   Give two piles of objects and ask: *How many have I got **altogether**?*

Adding using number lines

For the next stage, children still need to be counting real objects but they begin to use different types of number lines to support their calculation.

One example of this is a coloured beadstring. In school you may have seen a tray of red and white coloured beads on white strings. There will be 100 beads on each string, set out in alternating groups of 10 red, 10 white, 10 red, 10 white etc. all the way along. These beads slide along the string allowing the children to count as they move each bead.

A counting on addition problem might be:

A tree in the park was 6 m tall last year. Over the year it grew 2 m more. How tall is the tree now?

Using a beadstring count out the first 6 red beads and move them along the string to the empty end to represent the initial height of the tree (6 m). Then move the next 2 beads along to represent the extra 2 m and finally count up all the beads that have been moved.

The calculation will be recorded as:

6 + 2 = 8

And the answer is:

The tree is 8 m tall now.

As the numbers used get larger the children will begin to see that they don't have to count every bead every time because the beads are in groups of 10 red then 10 white.

So, using a beadstring to solve the calculation:

21 + 3 =

they first slide the two sets of 10 beads across to the empty end of the string along with one more bead so that 21 are moved in total. Next they move 3 more beads along to join the 21 so that the beadstring looks like this.

The children always count the groups of ten followed by the ones and so you hear: ten, twenty, twenty-one, twenty-two, twenty-three, twenty-four.

The tree question above is an example of a worded problem. Worded problems are a way of presenting a mathematical problem as a 'real-life' situation. Children are expected to read the problem, decide what calculation needs to be done to solve it and then decide what method they are going to use to get to the answer.

The bar method

Recently, a new way of helping children to solve worded problems has been introduced from the Singapore maths method. The Singapore approach recognises the value of being able to represent a calculation visually. Often children find it difficult to understand whether a word problem is asking them to add, subtract, multiply or divide but being able to 'draw' the problem often overcomes this difficulty. The bar is drawn with the top part representing the 'whole' or the larger number and the bottom part split up into sections, or 'parts', that add together to make the 'whole'. If we take the example of the trees above and represent it using the bar method this is:

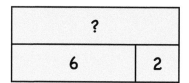

The lower 'bar' shows the two sections of the tree, the initial 6 m, followed by the extra 2 m that it grew. It is easy to see that what needs to be done now is to work out how much this is altogether so we can fill in the 'total' or 'whole' bar above. We always show the missing part of the calculation with a question mark to help us see which part we are trying to find.

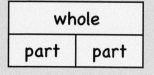
This method can be used to help children with worded problems for all four operations (i.e. addition, subtraction, multiplication and division) and indeed to solve fraction, decimal and percentage problems too. It is a very useful tool that many schools have adopted and have had a great deal of success with.

Labelled number lines

Pre-prepared number lines labelled from 0 to 10 or 0 to 20 are also often used to support and record calculations in preparation for Stage 3.

Let's take a look at how these support calculations using an addition worded problem.

I have 8 stickers and my friend gives me 3 more.
How many have I got now?

Using the bar method this gives:

?	
8	3

Using a number line start at 8 and then add on 3 more by drawing three hops of 1 to arrive at the number 11.

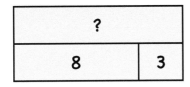

0 1 2 3 4 5 6 7 8 9 10 11 12 13 14 15 16 17 18 19 20

The calculation will be recorded as:

$$8 + 3 = 11$$

1   Draw out a number line and label it from 0 to 20. Gather items from around the home or the toy box and ask some addition questions using these items. Encourage your child to record the calculation on the number line. Make sure you ask some 'counting all' and 'counting on' questions.
For example:

For a counting all question build two lego towers and ask: *How many bricks are there altogether?*

For a counting on question build a tower of bricks and ask: *How many more bricks are needed to make a tower of 20?*

2   Practise number bonds up to 10. Give your child a number below 10 and ask them to make it up to 10. Ask questions that use number bonds to 10.

For example:

Barney has 6 chips on his plate. How many more does he need to make 10?

Vocabulary

Number bonds
Numbers that add together to make 10.

0 + 10	6 + 4
1 + 9	7 + 3
2 + 8	8 + 2
3 + 7	9 + 1
4 + 6	10 + 0
5 + 5	

3   When confident with numbers up to 10 try numbers up to 20.

For example:

If Asima has already hopped 13 m how many more metres does she need to hop to get to 20 m?

If you don't know about **count all** and **count on** questions please look back at the Introduction to addition page.

Adding using empty number lines

At the next stage, empty number lines are used to support addition calculations. An **empty number line** is a horizontal line drawn by children where they put the number they are adding onto at the beginning of the line. They then choose the size of hops best suited to the number they are adding on. This allows the child to add larger numbers by breaking down the number they are adding on into tens and ones and adding these in separate steps. Empty number lines are used for adding numbers larger than 20.

Let's consider the following problem:

Francis has 26p in his money box and his mum gives him the 23p change she gets when she goes shopping because he has been really helpful on the shopping trip. How much money does Francis have altogether now?

Using the bar method this gives us:

?	
26	23

From this problem the children will first be expected to write down the calculation they are going to solve in symbolic form, in other words:

26p + 23p =

Now to solve this by hopping on 23 ones from 26 is time consuming. So a quicker way is to hop the 20 first in 10s from 26 to 36 to 46, then the 3 in ones to get 47, 48, 49.

On the number line it looks like this:

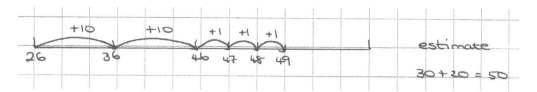

You may notice that alongside the calculation there is an **estimate** of the answer. Children are encouraged to get a rough idea of their answer by estimating first and writing this at the side of their page.

Vocabulary

Estimate
To get a rough idea of an answer - by rounding the numbers first to make them easier to calculate and then mentally performing the calculation.

As the children become more proficient with this method, and their ability to add multiples of ten mentally becomes more secure, they will start to see that they can add the tens in one hop and the ones in one hop as in the example below, making their method more efficient.

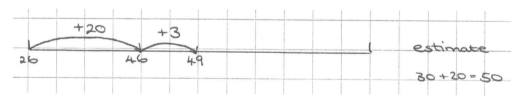

This second method can only be used if a really good understanding of partitioning has been obtained. **Partitioning** is the splitting of numbers into parts, in the case of 2-digit numbers into tens and ones, and for 3 digit numbers into hundreds, tens and ones. A significant amount of work is done on this at the beginning of every school year because it is fundamental in the mathematics strategies that are taught. If you find that your child struggles to 'partition' numbers help them practise at home.

Here are some partitioned numbers:

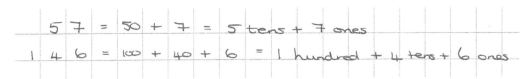

$$57 = 50 + 7 = 5 \text{ tens} + 7 \text{ ones}$$
$$146 = 100 + 40 + 6 = 1 \text{ hundred} + 4 \text{ tens} + 6 \text{ ones}$$

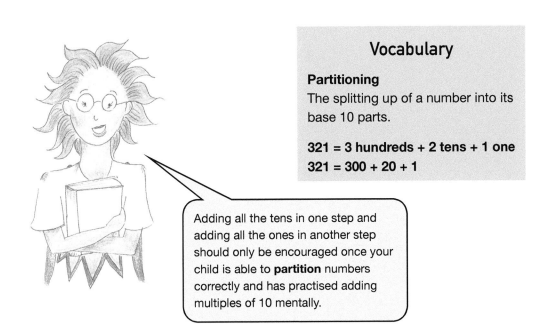

Vocabulary

Partitioning
The splitting up of a number into its base 10 parts.

321 = 3 hundreds + 2 tens + 1 one
321 = 300 + 20 + 1

Adding all the tens in one step and adding all the ones in another step should only be encouraged once your child is able to **partition** numbers correctly and has practised adding multiples of 10 mentally.

In that last problem we began with the number 26 and hopped on 23. If the problem had instead been:

Francis has 23p in his money box and his mum gives him the 26p change she gets when she goes shopping because he has been really helpful on the shopping trip. How much money does Francis have altogether now?

we still put the 26p first in the calculation, even though the smaller number has been given first in the worded problem. This is because it is usually more efficient to begin with the larger number and add on the smaller number.

Understanding the commutative law

We are able to switch these numbers around in our calculation because in addition we can use the **commutative law**. This law tells us that we can add numbers in any order and still get the same answer. In other words 2 + 4 = 4 + 2. The children are asked to explore this idea in separate maths lessons. They will be asked if they can find any numbers where they get a different answer if they add them in a different order.

Now let's work through another problem with slightly larger numbers.

46 tickets for a school concert are sold on Monday, 59 are sold on Tuesday. How many have been sold in total by the end of Tuesday?

The children will be guided through the following process:

1. Read the question carefully a few times and circle/highlight any key information.

46 tickets *for a school concert are sold on Monday,* **59** *are sold on Tuesday. How many have been sold* **in total** *by the end of Tuesday?*

2. Write down the calculation that needs to be done.

The word **total** *means add and the two numbers are* **46** *and* **59**.

Using the bar method this gives:

?	
46	59

The calculation will be:

$$46 + 59 =$$

3. Choose the preferred method to solve the calculation.

We are going to use an empty number line putting the largest number first.

4. Estimate the answer by rounding and adding mentally.

50 + 60 = 110

5. Do the calculation and check this against the estimate.

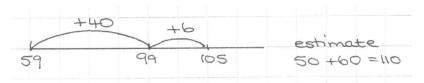

6. Answer the problem in a sentence.

105 tickets were sold in total.

1   Practise mentally adding 10, then multiples of 10, to different starting numbers.

   For example:

   If I have 67 stickers and am given 10 more, how many have I got now? What if I started with 35 stickers?

   If I have 48p and am given a 20p piece, how much will I then have? What if I was given 3 ten pence coins? 2 twenty pence coins? etc.

2   Count in multiples of 10 from a given starting number.

   For example:

   Count in tens from 34. So: 34, 44, 54, 64… etc

3   Partition 2-digit numbers into tens and ones.

   75 = 7 tens + 5 ones = 70 + 5

4   Move on to partitioning 3-digit numbers into hundreds, tens and ones.

Adding larger numbers using number lines

This stage is simply a development of the previous one to include larger numbers.

For example:

If 186 people travel by train to a pop concert and 78 travel by bus, how many have travelled by train or bus?

Using the bar method this gives:

?	
186	78

Using a number line it could be solved like this:

Firstly, an estimate is made by rounding each number to the nearest 10 and adding the numbers mentally. This is then recorded at the side of the page.

Next, the number line is drawn and labelled with the number 186 at the left end of the line.

The 78 passengers are partitioned into 70 and 8 and each of these parts is added onto the initial 186.

The answer of 264 is compared to the estimate of 270 and as it is similar it is taken as correct.

Finally, the answer is written out as a sentence:

264 people travelled to the concert by train or bus.

Compensation

The method above is perfectly fine and provides the correct answer. However, the calculation can be solved more easily by using **compensation**. Compensation is where you add (or take away) a small amount to (or from) a number in order to make that number easier to add on. After the addition you then adjust it back to 'compensate' for the amount you added on or subtracted in the first place. This is particularly useful when a number is very close to a multiple of 10 or 100.

For example, if I have to add 9 to 262 mentally I could count on 9 ones from 262, but it is easier to round the 9 to a 10 and add this to get 272. As I have now added 1 too many I adjust the answer back by subtracting the extra 1 to arrive at 271.

262 + 9 = 262 + 10 − 1 = 271

Vocabulary
Compensation
Used when adding or subtracting numbers that are close to a multiple of 10 - by rounding the number being added or subtracted to the nearest multiple of 10 and then adjusting the answer by the amount the number was rounded.
$35 + 11 = 35 + 10 + 1$
$35 - 11 = 35 - 10 - 1$
$35 + 9 = 35 + 10 - 1$
$35 - 9 = 35 - 10 + 1$

You can see that we can solve the previous calculation, 186 + 78 =, in less time and more easily using compensation by adding 80 and subtracting 2.

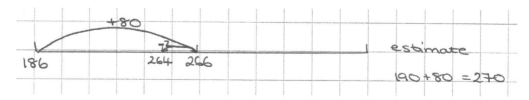

The calculation becomes:

186 + 80 – 2 =

Children are encouraged to look for the easiest way to solve their calculations and to know that often there is not one single correct way to solve a given calculation. The idea is that they have a good selection of methods, both mental and written, from which they can effectively choose the best method to solve a problem based on the size and type of the numbers in the problem.

It is important to stress that children should use the method of calculation they are most comfortable with. This will be dependent on their mental maths skills and the size/nature of the numbers involved.

1 Practise mentally adding the following numbers to different starting numbers:

9 by adding 10 and subtracting 1

19 by adding 20 and subtracting 1

99 by adding 100 then subtracting 1

98 by adding 100 and subtracting 2

2 Put the above calculations into worded problems.

For example:

Angelina has 344 lego bricks and is given 98 more. How many bricks does she have now?

Kieron buys a book for 67p and a pen for 19p. How much does this cost him altogether?

3 Continue to practise partitioning larger numbers in preparation for the next stage.

For example:

4,297 = 4,000 + 200 + 90 + 7

16,842 = 10,000 + 6,000 + 800 + 40 + 2

Adding by partitioning

The partitioning of numbers is revisited each year in primary school adding more of the base 10 **parts** (such as hundreds, thousands, ten thousands etc.) each time, moving from 2 digit numbers up to 9 digit numbers by the end of primary school.

For example:

$$7,296 = 7,000 + 200 + 90 + 6$$

$$26,324 = 20,000 + 6,000 + 300 + 20 + 4$$

Up to now partitioning has been used to help solve calculations mentally. The next stage is to use partitioning to help us move towards the column method of addition used by most adults, although don't expect the method you are familiar with to appear just yet!

Let's start with a calculation using smaller numbers while we learn the method.

$$76 + 47 =$$

To solve the calculation mentally first partition the numbers into:

$$70 + 6 \quad \text{and} \quad 40 + 7$$

Then gather the tens together and the ones together.

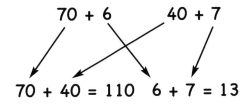

70 + 6   40 + 7

$$70 + 40 = 110 \quad 6 + 7 = 13$$

Finally add these answers together.

$$110 + 13 = 123$$

Vocabulary
Partitioning
The splitting up of a number into its base 10 parts
321 = 3 hundreds + 2 tens + 1 one
321 = 300 + 20 + 1

The children use the written method above and perform the parts of the calculation mentally. Once they are confident with this they are then shown how to set it out in a more formal way using columns:

We have the beginnings of a column method!

Again you can see we have estimated by rounding the tens and adding them. If our final answer is close to this answer it is likely to be correct.

A good grasp of partitioning numbers gained from practising adding numbers mentally is invaluable. So, if you've already been practising this with your child you will have helped enormously.

This method of laying out the numbers in the calculation shows clearly the value of the digits in each of the numbers.

Here's an example of a calculation solved by partitioning using three digit numbers.

What is the sum of 176 and 142?

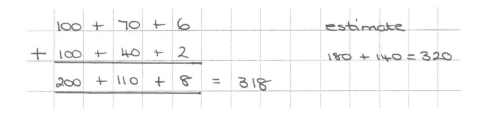

You may notice that the answers to these calculations have been estimated by rounding to the nearest 10. Your child will practise rounding in other maths lessons and will hopefully be using this skill to make sure the answers are 'about right'. If the estimate is very different from the calculated answer it is a warning to go back and check the working out, because something may have gone wrong. In both of the above calculations our estimates were close to our answers so all appears well!

Rounding

Now is a good time to look at rounding numbers in more detail. We round numbers to help us quickly arrive at an approximate figure when calculating mentally and an exact answer isn't necessary. We might use it to work out roughly what a shopping list costs to know if we have enough money in our purse, or to calculate the area of our lawn to see how much grass seed we need to buy. Crucially, estimating mentally first allows us to know if our written calculations seem about right. This is such a useful skill that the sooner a child can master it the better.

When rounding a number, we first need to decide how close to the original number it needs to be.

If, for example, we have the number **234,564** and round it to the nearest 10 this will give us **234,560** but it will still leave this number tricky to work with.

So we need to consider if this degree of accuracy is really necessary.

If it isn't we could consider rounding to the nearest 100 to get **234,600**, which is slightly easier to work with, or to the nearest 1,000 (**235,000**), 10,000 (**230,000**), or even 100,000 (**200,000**).

Rounding to the nearest 100,000 makes the number much easier to work with.

There is a system that helps us to round numbers that always works no matter how large the number.

Let's look at an example:

Round the number 2,346 to the nearest 10.

Firstly, identify the degree of accuracy needed, in this case to the nearest 10. Then, put an arrow above the digit in the number that corresponds to the degree of accuracy needed. Some children find it useful to write the column **place value headings** above the number, at least to begin with.

Vocabulary

Place value headings
The letters representing the value of the column the digit is in.

Th	H	T	O
2	3	4	6

So we need to put an arrow above the tens (T).

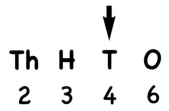

Next, underline the digit to the right - in this case it is the ones column.

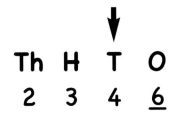

The rule now is: If the underlined digit is 5 or higher you round the digit with the arrow on it up by 1, if it is 4 or lower you round down (so the digit with the arrow above it stays the same). A good way for children to remember whether the digit rounds up or down is to associate it with doing a '**high five**' as 5 and higher round up.

Our digit is a 6 so we round the number up and it becomes:

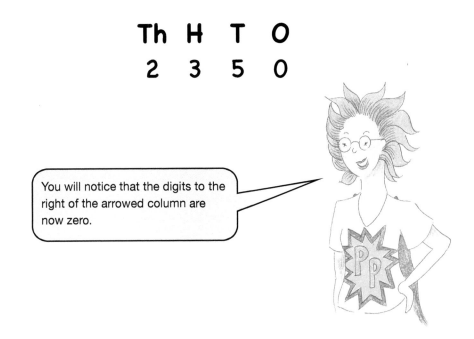

You will notice that the digits to the right of the arrowed column are now zero.

Let's work through the same process but rounding the number to the nearest 100 this time.

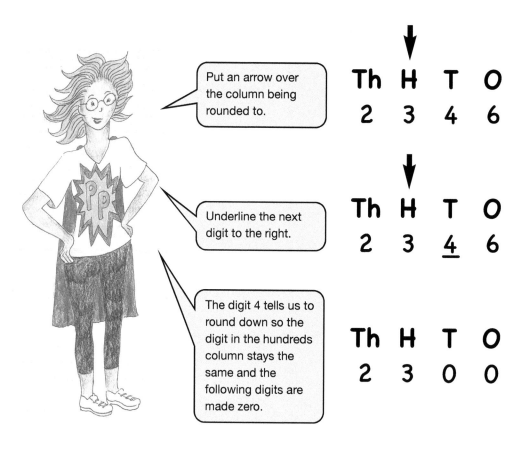

Put an arrow over the column being rounded to.

Th H T O
2 3 4 6

Underline the next digit to the right.

Th H T O
2 3 <u>4</u> 6

The digit 4 tells us to round down so the digit in the hundreds column stays the same and the following digits are made zero.

Th H T O
2 3 0 0

Vocabulary

Rounding
Changing a number to the nearest multiple of 10, 100, 1,000, 10,000 etc. to help make the number easier to work with when an exact answer isn't needed.

5 and higher rounds up
4 and lower rounds down

Remember this is the **'high five'** rule.

1   Practise rounding a number to the nearest 10.

   Start with a two digit number then move onto three or four digits.

   For example:

   Round 56 to the nearest 10. Round 245 to the nearest 10 etc.

2   Practise rounding other numbers to the nearest 100 or 1,000.

3   Practise estimating addition calculations by rounding to the nearest 10.

   For example: *Estimate 52 and 49 =   (= 50 + 50 = 100)*

                   Estimate 123 + 68 =   (=120 + 70 = 190)

4   Find times at home when you can use numbers in their real context to round or estimate totals.

   For example:

   What is the population of the UK to the nearest 100,000?

   Approximately how many grams of ingredients will there be in this receipe?

5   Worded problems often cause problems for children because they don't remember all the vocabulary that tells them to add. Make sure when you give them problems to solve you use a range of different vocabulary:

   *What is 3 **and** 7?*

   ***Add** 8 and 6.*

   *What is 5 **more than** 12?*

   *What is 24 **plus** 37?*

   ***Increase** 76 by 29.*

   *What is the **sum of** 129 and 48?*

   *Find the **total of** 69, 32 and 14.*

   *What are 1,294 and 742 **altogether**?*

This is the transitional step between the partitioning method of addition and the short method of column addition. It is called the **expanded column method** and places each worked out part of the calculation underneath each other rather than having them side by side. However, all of the worked steps are still clearly set out. This method is often taught alongside the partitioning method in the first instance so that the children can see where all the numbers in the new method come from.

Let's solve the the calculation we had in Stage 5 using firstly our partitioning method and then the expanded column method.

$$76 + 47 =$$

Partitioning Column Method

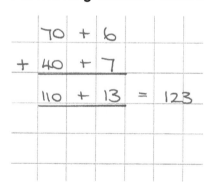

Expanded Column Method

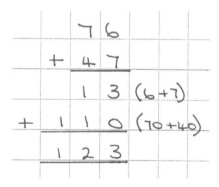

Children are asked to see if they can see the same numbers appearing in each method. They can see that we are completing the same mathematical steps in both methods but in the expanded column method we begin by adding the ones first, writing them in the correct column, then adding the tens and writing these underneath. Finally, we add the resulting two numbers, 13 and 110, by adding down each column from right to left.

Often, place value headings are used to aid understanding as in the next example.

It is 82 miles to my nan's house from my home and 35 miles from there to my auntie's house. If I go to visit my auntie, stopping off to say hello to my nan on the way, how far will I have travelled?

By this stage it is likely the child will recognise this problem as an addition and so will not need to use the bar method to show this.

This problem gives the calculation:

82 + 35 =

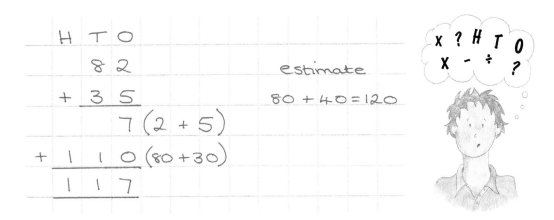

This stage should not be rushed. It is very important that your child really understands how the expanded column addition works before moving onto the next stage. Rushing on may mean that your child never truly understands how short column addition works. It may be that your child arrives at this stage during Key Stage 2 and does not go further for some time, even into Key Stage 3.

1   Practise adding two digit numbers.

For example: *Add up the ages of your parents.*

2   Move onto adding three or more two digit numbers.

For example: *Add up the ages of the people in your family.*

3   Move onto adding three digit numbers.

For example: *Add up the total runs in a cricket team.*

Add up the weight in grams of the ingredients in a cake.

7 years   35 years   31 years   6 years

Adding using the short column method

The short column method is where the concept of 'carrying below the line' is introduced.

Let's consider the problem:

Increase 267 by 155.

Estimate: Rounding to the nearest 10 gives us 270 + 160 = 430. We are expecting an answer close to 430.

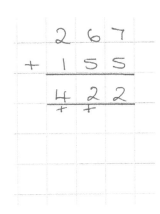

Again, to begin with we put the known method alongside the new method so that children can see how the numbers in both methods are linked.

To solve the calculation using the short column method begin by adding the ones digits together, in other words those in the right hand column. Adding the 7 and 5 ones gives 12. 'Carry' the 10 to the tens column and record it 'below the line' as a small 1 and place the 2 in the ones column. Next move to the tens column and add the digits in this column together, not forgetting to add the 1 that was 'carried' earlier, then cross out the 1, so you know that it's been added. Continue to add the hundreds in the same way.

Expanded Column Method

```
      2  6  7
  +   1  5  5
         1  2  (7 + 5)
      1  1  0  (60 + 50)
  +   3  0  0  (200 + 100)
      4  2  2
```

Short Column Method

```
      2  6  7
  +   1  5  5
      4  2  2
        ̶1 ̶1
```

Now let's look at a problem that involves even larger numbers.

Last Saturday 57,674 tickets were sold for the football match at Everton and 63,482 tickets were sold for the Liverpool match. How many tickets were sold in total?

This problem gives the calculation:

63,482 + 57,674 =

Using the short column method to solve this is:

Addition • Stage 7 • Adding using the short column method

Decimal numbers

The short column method can also be used to add decimal numbers. The important thing to remember here is to ensure that the decimal points are lined up underneath each other!

Let's consider the problem:

If Lei buys a new skirt for £17.90 and a brooch for 89p how much will she spend altogether?

Firstly, put both of the monetary values into the same units. Either pounds or pence can be chosen. In this case we've chosen pounds.

The calculation is:

£17.90 + £0.89 =

Estimate the answer by rounding to the nearest pound:

£18 + £1 = £19

And then calculate the answer:

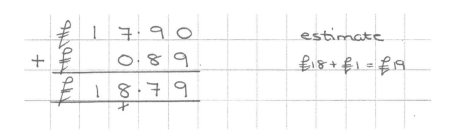

The answer in words is:

Altogether Lei will spend £18.79

1   Ask your child to add up some of the items on one of your shopping lists.

2   Provide a menu and ask questions from it that require the adding of two numbers.

For example:

How much would 2 pizzas cost?

How much would buying chicken and chips and a battered sausage cost?

3   Move onto adding three or more numbers.

For example:

How much would 3 pizzas cost?

How much would it cost for a curry, portion of rice and a naan bread?

4   Find a leaflet for a tourist attraction and ask how much it would cost for your family to attend.

5   Use an atlas and plan a trip to several countries.

Ask: *How many miles would we have to travel to complete the trip?*

6   Find the crowd capacity of different football grounds and find the total capacity for two or more of these.

7   Plan out the cost of a birthday party for a group of friends.

Subtraction

This chapter takes you through seven stages that lead to an understanding of **column subtraction**. These stages do not directly correspond to what is taught in each of the seven primary school years. Some stages will be passed through quite quickly and others will take much longer to fully understand and become confident in. For each stage, a few activities are provided for you to do with your child to support them with their school work.

Is all subtraction the same?

We use subtraction to solve problems based on one of the following concepts:

Take away – Taking one number from another. For example:

Mary has 7 stamps and her brother takes 3 of them. How many stamps has Mary got left?

Find the difference – Finding the difference between values, comparing one number to another number. For example:

Mary has got 7 stamps and her brother has got 3 stamps. How many more stamps has Mary got than her brother?

Find the complement – Finding how many more are needed to make a group complete. For example:

Mary has some red and blue stamps. If 3 out of the 7 stamps are blue how many are red?

Vocabulary

Take away
Taking one number from another.

Find the difference
Finding the difference between one number and another.

Find the complement
Making a group complete.

Subtracting by counting

Children begin learning subtraction by counting real objects to solve problems.

Let's look at each type of subtraction problem separately, starting with **take away**.

Here are some cars. How many are there? If I take 3 away how many are there now?

As this is a **take away** problem it can be solved by laying out the toy cars in a line, counting them, then removing 3 of them and recounting.

Pictorially

Numerically

$$7 - 3 = 4$$

Now let's look at a **find the difference** problem.

I have 3 cars and you have 7 cars. How many more cars have you got than me?

As this is a **find the difference** problem it can be solved by laying out the cars side by side and counting how many more there are in the longer line.

Pictorially

     1   2   3   4

Numerically

$$7 - 3 = 4$$

Finally, here is a **find the complement** problem.

I have 7 vehicles. 3 are cars and the rest are lorries. How many lorries are there?

As this is a **find the complement** problem it can be done by laying out 3 cars then counting on more vehicles to reach 7 altogether.

Pictorially

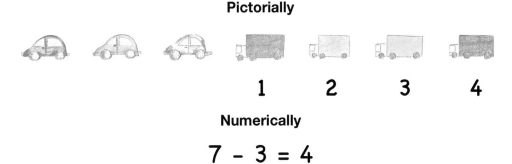

$$7 - 3 = 4$$

In the first example we solved the calculation by showing all the cars together and removing some by crossing them out.

In the second example we compared one set against another set.

In the third example we lined up the cars then continued the line using lorries until we reached the total number of vehicles.

There were three different types of problem, each solved differently but they all used the same calculation.

$$7 - 3 = 4$$

It is important for children to learn that they have the same subtraction calculation for all the three types of problem even if they are using a different method to solve it.

1 Practise with your child counting back in 1s from 10. Use your fingers to count with, begin by putting up all 10 fingers in front of you then putting down one finger at a time as you count each digit back from 10.

2 When your child is confident with this, try counting back from 20.

3 Practise counting back in 1s from different starting numbers.

4 Have a pile of toys.
Ask: *How many toys are there?*
Remove some and ask: *How many are there now?*

5 Have two piles of toys.
Ask: How many more are there in one pile than the other?

6 Have a pile of items made up of blue and red objects.
Ask questions like: *If there are 4 blue how many red are there?*

7 Try to use different words for subtract:
*What is 4 marbles **take away** 2 marbles?*
***Subtract** 4 bricks from 6 bricks.*
*What is 4 **less than** 8?*
*What is the **difference between** 6 and 3?*

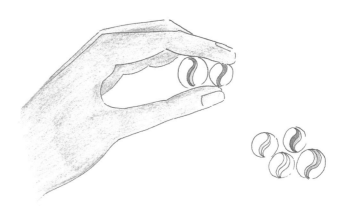

Once children are able to work confidently using real objects they begin to work with pictures of objects and items that represent the objects. This may include toys to represent real objects e.g. toy cars or some type of other 'counters'.

Beads on a beadstring are really good as counters and are often used at this stage.

If you would like more explanation about **beadstrings** see pages 8 and 9 in the Addition chapter.

Vocabulary

Worded problem
A mathematical problem written out in sentences, rather than as a calculation.

Let's consider a **take away** worded problem and see how a beadstring could help to solve it.

If I start with 12 stickers and then give 4 of them to my friend how many will I have left?

Using the bar method the problem looks like this:

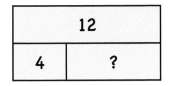

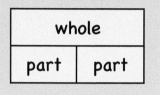
If you would like more explanation about the **bar method** see page 10 in the Addition chapter.

We are looking for the part of 12 that is left behind when 4 have been taken away. Using a beadstring slide 12 beads to the empty end of the string to represent the initial number of stickers.

To 'give 4 to my friend' slide the last 4 of these beads back to the full end of the beadstring. Count how many beads are left.

The calculation will be recorded as:

$$12 - 4 = 8$$

If children prefer not to use a beadstring they can use counters, coloured bricks or even stickers to solve the calculation. They just need to be able to gather up 12 of something, remove 4 and count how many are left.

Once the use of counters and beadstrings has been mastered, pre-prepared number lines are introduced. Initially the number lines are labelled from 0 to 10 for calculating with numbers up to 10. Later, when using numbers up to 20, the lines are labelled from 0 to 20.

Let's use a labelled number line to solve the calculation:

12 – 4 =

We begin at 12 and hop back 4 in ones to land on the number 8.

The calculation will be recorded as:

12 – 4 = 8

The answer to the problem is:

I will have 8 stickers left.

1   Encourage your children to practise using their fingers to subtract numbers up to 10.

2   Use any counter type objects you have at home. These could be counters from a game, marbles, lego bricks, 1p coins etc. Practise **taking away, finding the difference** or **finding the complement.**

For example:

If I have 10p at the start of the day and spend 6p, how much have I got left?

If there are 12 marbles in this pile and 7 marbles in this pile, which pile is bigger? By how much?

I have 9 pieces of fruit. Some are apples and some are pears. If I have 4 apples, how many pears are there?

3   Draw out a number line and label 0 to 20. Using items from around the home, or the toy box, create some subtraction questions, or make up some questions based on activities your child enjoys and solve them using the number line.

For example:

If there are 11 children in your football team and 5 have black boots, how many don't have black boots?

> If you don't know about **take away, find the difference** and **find the complement** questions please look back at the Subtraction introduction page.

Subtracting using empty number lines

As the numbers being used in calculatons get larger, hopping along the number line in ones becomes very time consuming, so an empty (blank) number line is used where children can choose the size of the hops themselves.

There are two different methods for using an empty number line and the method chosen is determined by the nature of the problem i.e. whether it is a **take away**, **find the difference** or **find the complement** problem.

> If you would like more explanation about **empty number lines** see page 13 in the Addition chapter.

Let's consider each of the types of problem in turn:

Lorenzo has 25 cubes and Sian has 13. How many more cubes does Lorenzo have than Sian?

Using the bar method to visualise the problem gives us:

Lorenzo	25	
Sian	13	?

Here we recorded how many cubes Lorenzo had in the top bar and the amount Sian had (the smaller amount) in the bottom bar. This will show us how many more we would need to add to Sian's amount to get to Lorenzo's amount.

This is a **find the difference** problem.

Having worked out that this is a subtraction problem children will be expected to write down the calculation they are going to solve in symbolic form, in other words:

25 – 13 =

To solve it using an empty number line we begin by drawing our own line and putting 13 at the left end of the line and 25 at the right end (we always put the smaller number at the beginning of the line and the larger number at the far end, no matter what the order of the numbers). Next, we work from the smaller number to the larger one by **adding on**. First, we add as many tens as we can and then add the rest in ones. We record how much we've added above each 'hop'. The method looks like this:

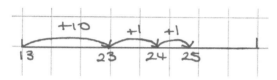

Finally, we add up the value of each hop to find out the total **difference**.

10 + 1 + 1 = 12

The answer will be:

Lorenzo has 12 more cubes than Sian.

Let's now look at a **take away** problem:

Anita has 25 pencils and gives 13 away.
How many has she got now?

Using the bar method this gives:

25	
13	?

We are now recording how many pencils we started with - the 'whole' on the top bar and the amount taken away as a 'part' of the bottom bar. The idea is to find how many are left.

This is now a **take away** question so, although the bar looks the same, the empty number line is used slightly differently.

We put the number we start with (25) at the righthand end of the line as before. However, this time we **hop back** the amount we are taking away (13). We first hop back the 10 in one step then the 3 in single steps of one. The number we finish on is the answer.

The method looks like this:

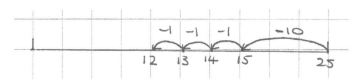

You can see that there is a minus sign in front of the numbers that we 'hopped' to show that we have taken away that amount each time. We hopped -10 -1 -1 -1 to hop -13 altogether. We end up on the number 12 and so our calculation is:

25 − 13 = 12

And the answer is:

Anita has 12 pencils now.

Finally, let's look at a **find the complement** problem.

I have 25 crayons. 13 are yellow and the rest are blue. How many are blue?

Using the bar method this is:

25	
13	?
Yellow	Blue

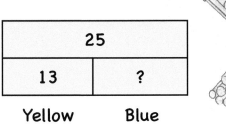

Here the bar method shows the total number of crayons in the top bar and the parts that are yellow and blue in the bottom bar.

This is solved in the same way as the 'find the difference' problem. There are 13 yellow crayons and we need to find how many more will make it up to 25 crayons. The best way to do this is to use the number line method of **adding on**.

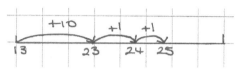

So the answer is:

There are 12 blue crayons.

When larger numbers are used in calculations children will move on to subtracting multiples of ten in one 'hop' and groups of ones in one 'hop'.

Let's consider a **take away** problem with slightly larger numbers and hop back in these larger 'hops':

If Diane has 35 crisps in her packet and eats 24 of them. How many are left?

Using the bar method this gives:

35	
24	?

The calculation for this problem is:

35 – 24 =

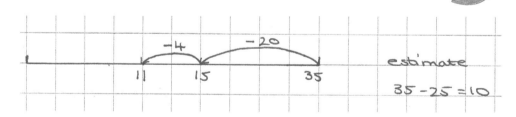

It can be solved by taking away the 20 from 35 in one hop first to give 15, then taking away the 4 in one hop to give the answer 11.

So the answer is:

Diane has 11 crisps left.

As the numbers are slightly larger now I make a rough **estimate** of the answer first by rounding the numbers to the nearest 5 and then mentally solving the calculation. (For more information about rounding see page 26 of the Addition chapter.) I jot down my estimate at the side of the page so I can check it against my answer later. As the numbers are close to each other my answer is likely to be correct.

Crossing the tens boundary

Some subtraction calculations require the crossing of the tens boundary. This happens when the larger number ends with a low digit and the number that is being taken away ends with a high digit e.g. 72 - 49 = . To solve a calculation like this, first hop back the tens (in this case 40) then hop back to the nearest multiple of ten in ones (which in this example is to 30) then hop back any remaining ones.

72 − 49 =

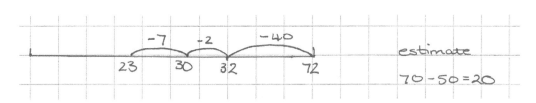

However, sometimes children prefer to subtract the ones in a single step by counting back on their fingers. They would then record their working out as in the example below.

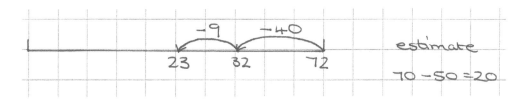

Worded problems

Often children struggle with subtraction worded problems because they don't always understand which numbers they are subtracting from which. They often assume that the number that comes first in the problem will be the number that comes first in the subtraction calculation, but this is not always the case. This can be seen in the examples below.

Example 1:

If Hemakshi earns £65 and Haroon earns £98. How much more has Haroon earned than Hemakshi?

Here the bar method is particularly helpful. It makes it obvious what the calculation should be. The question asks how much more one is than the other so the longer bar, showing the larger amount, goes at the top.

Haroon	98	
Hemakshi	65	?

The calculation is:

98 − 65 =

Example 2:

257 tickets out of 487 have been sold for a tennis match. How many are there left to sell?

Using the bar method this gives us:

487	
257	?

The calculation is:

487 − 257 =

At Stage 3, the **largest** number is always the first one in a subtraction calculation. However, in later stages this is sometimes not the case. The children will soon be completing more challenging problems that may give negative number answers, where the smaller number may be put first should a problem require it.

It is essential therefore that children understand that subtraction, unlike addition, is **not commutative** and that it **does** matter which order the numbers are in the calculation.

Let's consider problems that use the phrasing **subtract from**.

Subtract 17 from 25.

This gives us:

$$25 - 17 = 8$$

Subtract 37 from 24.

This gives us:

$$24 - 37 = -13$$

We need to understand the wording of a problem in order to solve it correctly.

Vocabulary

Commutative Law
Addition and multiplication are commutative as you can swap the numbers round and get the same answer.

This is not the case for subtraction and division.

$$2 + 4 = 4 + 2 \qquad 4 - 2 \neq 2 - 4$$
$$2 \times 4 = 4 \times 2 \qquad 4 \div 2 \neq 2 \div 4$$

Negative numbers

In preparation for calculations involving negative numbers children start to practise mentally counting forward and back through zero and 'hopping' forward and back on a number line labelled from -10 through zero to +10

One way to think of negative numbers is as **the amount you owe** or as **debt**.

For example it can be explained as:

If I borrow £5 to buy a favourite book when I have no pocket money, then I will need to pay back that £5 when I next get some money. My pocket money balance would show -£5 until I pay the money back. If I then earn £2 my new bank balance would show -£3, and so on until the debt is completely paid.

Below are some simple problems to practise negative numbers.

Example 1:

If Ayesha has £3 in her piggy bank and spends £7 on a new book. How much will she owe?

On the number line begin on the number 3 and hop back the £7 spent on the book to arrive at the number -4.

Remember negative numbers are the amount owed.

The answer is:

Ayesha will owe £4.

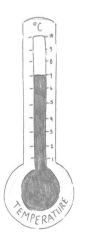

Example 2:

The temperature in the evening was 7°C. Overnight it went down by 10 degrees. What is the temperature now?

On the number line begin on the number 7 and hop back the 10°C to arrive at the number -3.

The answer is:

The temperature is now -3°C.

Inverse

Children are taught that addition and subtraction are the inverse of each other. In other words, subtraction undoes addition and addition undoes subtraction. This is very useful in helping us check answers to calculations.

Let's solve a worded problem using subtraction then check it using an addition calculation:

35 out of 73 football matches played were won or drawn, how many were lost?

Using the bar method this gives:

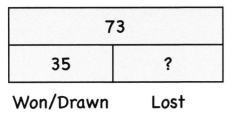

Won/Drawn   Lost

The problem is solved using the calculation:

$$73 - 35 =$$

Estimating and solving using the number line gives:

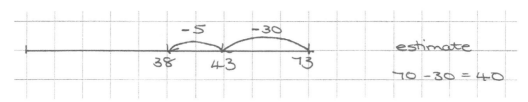

The answer is:

38 matches were lost.

Now let's check this answer using the inverse calculation:

35 + 38 =

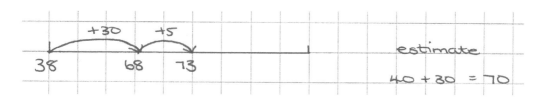

By arriving back at the starting number, **73**, it confirms that the calculation is correct. If we had got any other number at the end of the second calculation we would have to consider whether we had made an error either in the first calculation or the second. We would be alerted to the need to go back and check our work!

Missing number problems

Most calculations have the numbers in the calculation on the left hand side of the equals sign and space for the answer you're trying to find on the right hand side of the equals sign. For example:

34 – 24 = ☐

A missing number problem has the space for the missing number somewhere else in the calculation. For example:

34 – ☐ **= 10**   or   ☐ **– 13 = 4**

Missing number problems are often tricky for children because it is not immediately clear what they need to do to solve them.

There are different rules to help solve missing number problems depending on whether the calculation is an addition, subtraction, multiplication or division and where the missing number is in the calculation. We will only consider the addition and subtraction calculations in this section. Addition and subtraction need to be considered together because subtraction can be used to solve addition missing number problems and addition is sometimes used to help solve subtraction missing number problems.

Trying to decide on the method to solve missing number problems becomes much easier if the bar method is used to represent the problem.

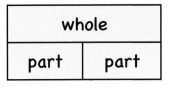

Let's consider the addition calculation:

$$37 + \boxed{} = 69$$

Using the bar method this is:

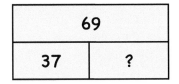

The bar method diagram shows that we need to subtract the part from the whole to find the missing part.

The calculation is:

$$69 - 37 =$$

This can now be solved in the usual way.

If we have the missing number on the left side of the operator, as in:

$$\boxed{} - 26 = 58$$

Using the bar method this is:

The bar method diagram shows that we need to add the two parts together to make the whole.

The calculation is:

$$26 + 58 =$$

This can now be solved in the usual way.

Now let's look at a subtraction calculation with the missing number after the operator:

$$74 - \boxed{} = 28$$

Using the bar method this is:

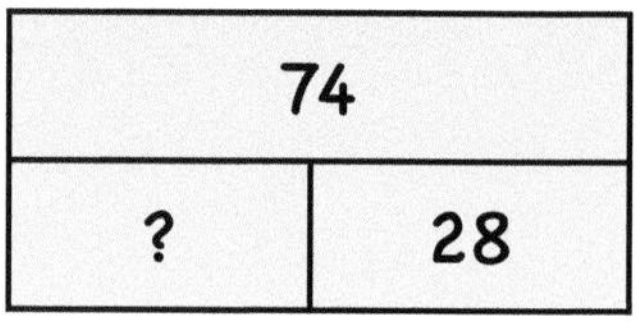

74	
?	28

This bar method diagram shows that we need to subtract the part from the whole to find the missing part.

The calculation is:

$$74 - 28 =$$

This can now be solved in the usual way.

The general rules are:

In an addition missing number problem, a subtraction calculation is needed to solve it.

In a subtraction calculation with the first number missing, an addition calculation is needed to solve it.

In a subtraction calculation with the second number missing, a subtraction calculation is needed to solve it.

1   Count back in ones from different starting numbers.
    For example: begin at 27, 59 or 105.

2   Move onto subtracting numbers below 10 from different starting numbers.
    For example: *45 – 3 =   53 – 9 =*

3   Count back in tens from different starting numbers.
    For example: begin at 75 or 132.

4   Move onto subtracting multiples of ten from different numbers.
    For example: *92 – 40 =   87 – 30 =*

5   Make a number line labelled -10 to 10. Practise counting back and forwards
    through zero.

6   Ask some worded questions and use the negative
    number line.

    For example: *If you start with £5 and want to buy a
    doll for £8 how much will you need to borrow?
    What would your bank balance show?*

7   Ask questions to encourage the use of inverse.
    For example: *I think the answer to 47 + 38 is 75.
    Can you check it using 2 different subtraction calculations?*
    (*75 – 47 =   75 – 38 =*)
    What is the correct answer?

Children will now begin to use larger numbers on the number line (up to 3 digits).

Let's look at one of each type of subtraction problem using the same numbers and how the number line will be used in each instance.

Here is an example of a **find the complement** problem:

237 tickets out of a total of 750 tickets have been sold. How many tickets are there left to sell?

Using the bar method this gives:

750	
237	?

A good way to solve a find the complement question is by **adding on.** We use the same method as in Stage 3 but with the larger numbers more hops will be needed.

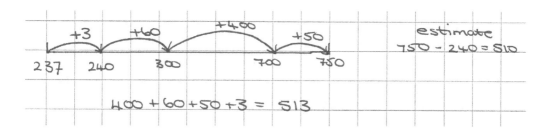

Here we added on 3 ones to take us to the next multiple of 10 (240), next we added on tens up to the next multiple of 100 (300), we then added on any hundreds to take us to the hundreds in the final number (700), and finally we added the tens to arrive at 750.

The method is like addition but instead of **adding on** a given amount we add up to a given amount and then count up how much we have **added on**.

The calculation is recorded as:

750 – 237 = 513

And the answer is:

There are 513 tickets left to sell.

An example of a **take away** problem is:

There were 750 butterflies in a butterfly farm. 237 of them escaped. How many butterflies are there left?

Using the bar method to represent this it would look exactly the same as the previous example.

However, because we are taking away from 750 this time our calculation method will be different. We place 750 at the righthand end of the line and **hop back** the 237 in partitioned steps; 200 then 30 then 7.

The calculation is recorded as:

750 – 237 = 513

And the answer is:

There are 513 butterflies left.

An example of a **find the difference** problem is:

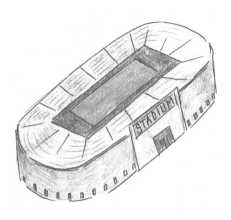

There are 750 Liverpool football fans at a football match and 237 Everton fans. How many more Liverpool fans are there than Everton fans?

Here we are looking for the **difference between** two numbers, so we place the two numbers at each end of the line then find out how far it is from one to the other. This is done by **adding on**.

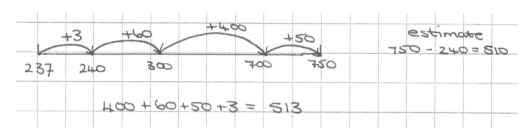

The calculation is recorded as:

750 – 237 = 513

And the answer is:

There are 513 more Liverpool fans than Everton fans.

Both the **find the complement** and **find the difference** problems used the same number line method, that of adding on by hopping in steps from the smallest number to the largest number. The **take away** problem used hopping back from the largest number to the smallest number. Of course both methods will always give us the same result!

Activities to help at home

1   Practise mental subtraction by giving a three digit number and subtracting ones. Use large digits in the initial number and only take away values that do not require you to pass through the tens boundary.

For example: $768 - 6 =$

2   Give a three digit number and subtract multiples of ten. Use large digits in the initial number and only take away values that do not require you to pass through the hundreds boundary.

For example: $768 - 40 =$

3   Give a three digit number and subtract multiples of a hundred.

For example: $768 - 200 =$

4   Repeat using numbers that cross the tens and hundreds boundaries.

For example: $321 - 6 =$

$321 - 40 =$

5   Begin with the number: 999

Roll a dice three times to make another three digit number.

Subtract this from 999 using a number line.

(this will not need your child to cross through the tens or hundreds boundaries)

6   Begin with the number: 123

Roll a dice twice to make a two digit number.

Subtract this from 123 using a number line.

(this may need your child to cross through the tens or hundreds boundaries)

Subtracting using partitioning column method

Children will have been using partitioning to help them subtract mentally already but they now use it to help them work towards a column method.

Let's start by solving calculations with smaller numbers while we learn the new method.

Numbers that don't need an **exchange** are used first. This is where the digit in the ones column of the first number is larger than the digit in the ones column in the number being subtracted.

For example:

$$79 - 47 =$$

To solve the above calculation **partition** 79 into 70 + 9 and **partition** 47 into 40 + 7 and arrange as in the picture below. Beginning at the top of the ones column subtract the bottom number from the top number (9 - 7 = 2) then move onto the tens column and subtract (70 - 40 = 30). Finally, add the two parts of the answer together (30 + 2 = 32).

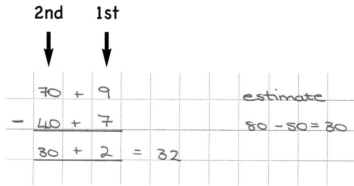

You can see that we have an add sign between the tens and ones digits. This signifies that the numbers are 70 + 9, representing the number 79, and 40 + 7 representing the number 47.

However, this method so far is clearly limited because many calculations will not have the ones digit in the first number larger than that in the second, as in the calculation 56 – 27 = where the 6 is smaller than the 7. We need a strategy that allows us to subtract any number from another number whatever their digits. The method we use is **decomposition**. Decomposition is where we **exchange** 1 of a larger unit for 10 smaller ones whilst still keeping the same value of the original number.

Vocabulary

Decomposition
The breaking down of a number into its base 10 parts.

1 ten = 10 ones
1 hundred = 10 tens
1 thousand = 10 hundreds

In order to solve the calculation

56 – 27 =

a ten from the 50 needs to be swapped, or **exchanged,** for 10 ones to add to the 6 already there so that we can subtract 7 from it. Using the partitioning method the final calculation would then look like this:

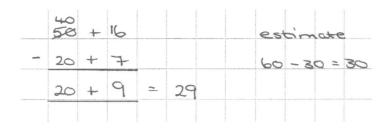

This method explicitly shows what is happening to the ten that is taken from the tens column and given to the ones column.

Vocabulary

Exchange
The transfer of one of the tens for 10 ones or one of the hundreds for 10 tens in order to solve a subtraction calculation.

One of the most common problems in solving subtraction calculations comes from not spending enough time consolidating this stage. The two important things to remember are:

1   You must subtract reading down the column - starting with the top number and subtracting the bottom number from it.

2   If there isn't enough to subtract from because the number at the top is smaller than the number below, you **must exchange**.

Here is an example where a child has not understood one or both of these principles. This is an extremely common mistake!

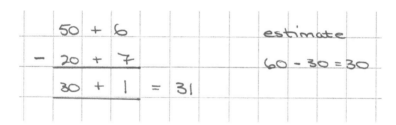

The mistake is that a ten has not been taken from the 50 and given to the 6 to make 16 and then 7 subtracted from the 16 reading down the column. Instead the smaller number 6 was subtracted from the larger number 7 by reading up the column.

'51s' game

There is an excellent game to help children learn about **decomposition** called 51s. If it is played enough times children will become so familiar with exchanging a ten for ten ones that by the time they need to use it in their calculations they will do it automatically. This is a game that your child would benefit from playing at home.

The rules:

This is a game for 2 players.

Equipment: 10 ten sticks, 30 unit blocks, dice

The aim of the game is to be the first player to get rid of all their blocks.

Each player begins with 51 made up of 5 ten sticks and 1 unit block.

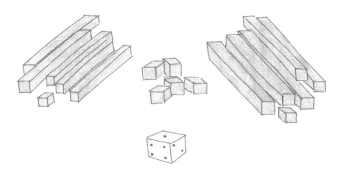

In school, base ten equipment is used which consist of plastic sticks made of 10 unit sized blocks and single unit blocks. You could use something from home to represent the sticks and unit blocks; 10 lego bricks pressed together for the sticks and single lego bricks for the ones are ideal, alterantively use pencils for sticks worth 10 units, and buttons or beads could be used to represent the single units.

There needs to be a spare pile of unit blocks placed between the two players.

Both players roll the dice. The player with the highest number goes first.

Player 1 rolls the dice and takes away the number of unit blocks displayed on the dice from their pile. If they haven't got enough unit blocks they **must** exchange a ten stick for 10 unit blocks first.

Player 2 takes the next turn and play continues alternately, throwing the dice and removing the number of unit blocks displayed.

(Note: you are not allowed to exchange if you have enough unit blocks in your pile already to discard the number shown on the dice.)

Whoever gets rid of all their blocks first wins!

Subtracting 3 digit numbers

As soon as the the partitioning column method is secure, children begin to work with larger numbers again.

Let's take the calculation we looked at at the end of Stage 4, that uses 3-digit numbers, and solve it using the partitioning column method.

750 – 237 =

The method looks like this:

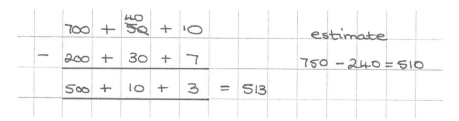

We exchanged a ten from the initial 50 in 750 so that we could subtract the 7 ones from the 10.

The answer 513 is close to our estimate of 520 so it looks likely that our answer is correct.

Both of the examples in this Stage have needed us to exchange a ten for ten ones but we can exchange in any column if we need to, as long as we remember to exchange for ten of the next column to the right. For example: a hundred could be exchanged for ten tens, a thousand can be exchanged for ten hundreds.

Now is a good time to ensure your child knows the words associated with subtraction that are likely to be asked in Key Stage 2.

Vocabulary

Subtraction

take away	take from
subtract	less than
minus	decrease
reduce	fewer
difference between	

1   Play the 51s game - explained on page 64.

2   Worded problems that require subtraction often cause difficulties for children because they don't remember all the vocabulary that tells them to subtract. They also need to decide which number to put first in the calculation. Make sure when you give children problems to solve you use all the different vocabulary so that they become familiar with it.

For example:

*What is 46 **take away** 27?*

***Take** 14 **from** 50.*

***Subtract** 38 from 75.*

*What is 5 **less than** 21?*

*What is £65 **minus** £24?*

*What is the **difference between** 294 and 142?*

***Decrease** 76 by 29.*

***Reduce** 129 by 48?*

*What is 94 **fewer than** 137?*

Following on from the partitioning column method, children begin to use the column method with decomposition. The difference between these methods is only small but the new method requires the child to fully understand the value of each digit in the numbers. Teaching the two methods at the same time helps children to understand the worth of each digit.

Let's consider the following problem, solving it by using both methods side by side:

Take 427 from 932.

Partitioning Column Method   Column Method

The difference in the two methods above is simply that we have written out each number into it's partitioned parts in the first method whereas we have left the number unpartitioned in the second. You can also see that in the second method we have labelled the columns with the letters HTO (hundreds, tens, ones) to help the children to remember as they use this new method the value of each digit in the number. Once this understanding is secure the headings no longer need to be used as in the example below.

At this stage, if children have not understood that subtraction is **NOT commutative** or have not grasped that you must work **down** the columns errors can easily occur. Unfortunately, errors do occur quite often because children are either encouraged to move on from the partitioning method before they are ready, or they have tried to move themselves on too quickly.

Children often avoid using decomposition either because it seems trickier to do or simply that their eyes see the two digits separately and simply automatically take the smaller one from the larger one. One way to address this issue is to look at the ones column in the calculation (in our case 932 - 427 =) and give the child 2 pencils to represent the digit in the ones column of 932. Next ask them to take away 7 pencils taken from the ones digit in the number 427. They soon see the problem! It is important to show that if you then give them 10 more pencils by exchanging a ten from the 30 in 932 then 7 pencils can now be taken away.

More practise playing the 51s game will also help.

Do not be worried about having to go back to using the partitioning method for a while to give your child more time to understand the principles of decomposition. It will pay dividends later.

1   Play the 51s game.

2   Ask your child to find the inverse to check calculations.

For example:

I increased 345 by 176 and got the answer 531. Is this correct?

Subtract 165 from 435. Check your answer using addition.

654 minus 321 is 333. True or False?

3   Find a pack of cards and remove the picture cards. Turn over 3 cards and make the largest number you can from the three digits displayed laying the cards out on the table. Turn over another three cards and make the smallest number you can. Decide which of these two numbers is the largest. Put this number at the top and subtract the smaller one from it.

4   Draw out a 3 x 3 grid and put the number 999 in the top boxes. Roll a dice three times to make another three digit number and write this directly underneath. Subtract the bottom number from the top number using column subtraction. (This will not need your child to use exchange.)

9	9	9

5   Draw out another 3 x 3 grid and this time put the number 123 in the top boxes. Roll a dice twice to create a two digit number and write this directly underneath in the tens and ones columns. Subtract the bottom number from 123 using column subtraction. (This may need your child to use exchange.)

1	2	3

Once the column method is secure children move onto using it to subtract both larger numbers and decimal numbers which may have 4 or more digits in them.

Let's look at a typical worded problem that uses four digit decimal numbers:

If one pair of trainers costs £37.49 and another pair costs £23.72, how much more does the expensive pair cost?

By this stage it is hoped that the children already recognise this as a subtraction problem and so would not draw out the bar method to represent it.

The calculation needed to solve the problem is:

£37.49 – £23.72 =

The important factor for the column method to be successful here is to make sure the decimal points are lined up one under another because this then ensures that all the other digits will be in the correct place for calculating.

Let's solve the calculation using the column method.

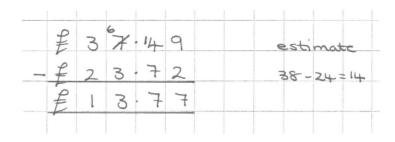

You may notice that we rounded both of the numbers up to the nearest whole pound when we estimated, even though £37.49 is actually closer to £37 than £38. We did this to keep the estimated answer closer to the exact answer after the numbers have been subtracted.

The estimated answer is close to the calculated answer so we can assume the calculation is correct.

The answer to the problem is:

The expensive trainers cost £13.77 more.

Children are shown several methods of solving subtraction calculations as they move through the school. Although they will eventually become proficient in using column subtraction with decomposition it doesn't necessarily mean that this method should always be used. Children need to be able to select the **best** method for the numbers involved in the calculation.

Children are asked firstly to decide if they can solve the problem mentally, and if they can then this is how they should do it. If the numbers are tricky or too large for easy mental calculation the children are encouraged to choose the best written method of the ones they know to solve the problem efficiently.

To illustrate this, let's use different methods to solve the calculation below and then decide which is the most efficient.

Reduce 20,000 by 19,897.

You may feel that you can solve this mentally, in which case go ahead. That's great. If you don't feel confident, on the other hand, then that's fine too. There are a couple of choices. As long as you have progressed to the **column method using decomposition** you won't need to use **partitioning** but you could also choose the **number line method** we learnt at Stage 4.

Here are both methods side by side.

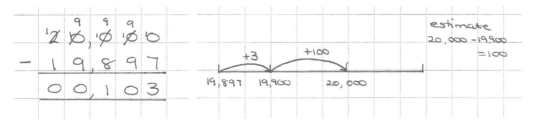

The answer to the problem is:

$$20,000 - 19,897 = 103$$

In the column method we need to decompose four different digits. There is a lot of opportunity here for making mistakes. A very common mistake children make when subtracting from large multiples of 10, 100, 1,000, 10,000 etc. (in this case 20,000) is that of trying to exchange 1 of the large multiples, say the 10,000, for 10 ones. This clearly isn't a **fair** or **equal** exchange and will give the wrong answer to the calculation. If this happens it shows that more work needs to be done to understand **decomposition**.

When a mistake occurs using the column method, children are asked to check their answer either by completing an inverse calculation or by using the number line method instead.

We can see that the calculation is easier to solve using the number line method, especially if it is solved by **adding on**, as shown in the example above. We want to encourage children to see that calculations that involve numbers that are **close in value** are best solved this way.

A version of the number line method is often used to solve calculations mentally, by adding onto the smaller number to reach the larger number.

This stage is about encouraging the most efficient method of calculation rather than expecting the latest method that has been taught to be used.

1   Look at the prices in a brochure of items your child might like to have. Choose an item.

Ask: *How much change would you get if you paid for it with a £10 note?*

2   Move onto buying multiple items and larger pound note denominations to encourage the use of adding and subtracting in the same problem.

3   Look up information about a favourite sporting team. Ask questions from different matches.

For example: *How many more home fans are there than away fans?*

Your child could work this out for each match over the whole season.

4   Look at an atlas. Ask questions about the distance between places.

For example: *How much further is it from London to Tokyo than from London to Paris?*

5   Look up populations of different countries on the internet. Ask questions about these.

For example: *How many more people live in China than Russia?*

This can be interesting to discuss when you consider the size of the countries too.

6   For even larger numbers compare the distances of different planets from Earth.

Multiplication

This chapter takes you through seven stages that lead to an understanding of **column multiplication**. It progresses from multiplying using repeated addition through the number line method, the partitioning method, the grid method to the column method itself. The last two stages take the grid and column methods further using larger and decimal numbers.

Why do we need to multiply?

We use multiplication for one of two reasons either as **repeated addition** or to **scale** an amount up or down.

If we want to find the total of several sets of equally sized groups we could simply add the sets up as in the following example:

If there are 3 packets of pencils with 10 pencils in each packet how many pencils are there altogether?

We add 3 lots of 10.

$$10 + 10 + 10 = 30$$

This method is called **repeated addition** - we repeatedly add the same amount.

However, when we want to find the total of a larger number of groups, for example the amount of pencils in 7 packets, 13 packets or even 345 packets, using repeated addition is cumbersome and prone to errors. Other methods of multiplication allow us to find the total of a repeated addition problem in a much more efficient way.

Multiplication is also used to **scale** a quantity or measurement up or down.

Vocabulary

Repeated addition
adding sets of equally sized goups together.

Scale
Making a quantity or measurement a number of times bigger or smaller.

For example:

Tom's garden is 7 m long. Henry's garden is three times longer than Tom's. How long is Henry's garden?

To find the length of Henry's garden we need to scale Tom's garden up by multiplying its length by 3. So, if Tom's garden is 7 metres long Henry's garden can be found by the calculation:

3 lots of 7 = 21 metres

We can also scale down by multiplying by a number less than 1.

Tom's garden is 7 m long. Henry's garden is half as long as Tom's. How long is Henry's garden?

Half the length of Tom's garden will be **½ of 7** which is calculated as:

½ x 7 = 3½ metres.

Multiplying using repeated addition

At this stage multiplication is used to perform repeated addition. Real objects, or pictures of real objects, are laid in sets where each set has the same number of items in it. The total number of items can then be counted in steps, where the size of the step is the number of items in the group.

Let's consider the problem:

How many cars are in 4 lots of 2 cars?

 2

 4

Arranging the cars in rows of 2 gives us:

 6

Adding up all the cars by counting in 2s gives us the answer:

 8

There are 8 cars altogether.

Let's consider the problem:

How many fingers are on 6 hands?

To find the answer, if there are enough people, we can hold up 6 hands and then count the fingers in 5s, or if not we can use a picture of 6 hands and count the fingers in 5s.

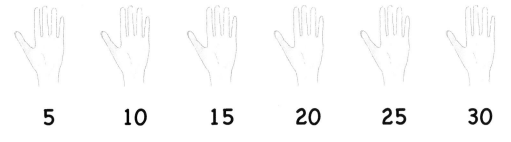

| 5 | 10 | 15 | 20 | 25 | 30 |

Adding up all the fingers gives us the answer:

There are 30 fingers altogether.

We could record the calculation pictorially as above or numerically in one of the ways below:

6 lots of 5 is 30

6 times 5 is 30

6 multiplied by 5 is 30

6 x 5 = 30

Let's consider the problem:

How many pencils are there in 4 packets of 10 pencils?

We solve this by counting in sets of 10.

We can record the calculation in any of the following ways:

Pictorially

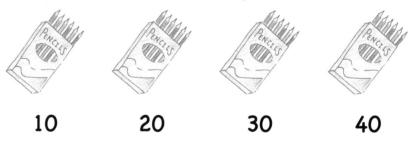

| 10 | 20 | 30 | 40 |

Numerically

4 lots of 10 is 40   **4 times 10 is 40**

4 multiplied by 10 is 40 or **4 x 10 = 40**

Whichever way we choose to record the calculation, adding up all the pencils by counting in 10s gives us the answer:

There are 40 pencils altogether.

Activities to help at home

1   Practise counting objects in groups of 2. Think about what items naturally come in 2s wherever you can, like socks, hands, feet, shoes, because this will make the counting more meaningful.

2   Move on to counting objects in groups of 10 then 5.

3   Try to get a rhythm going when counting in 2s, 5s or 10s because this will help with fluency.

4   Write out counting in 2s as 2, 4, 6, 8, 10, 12, 14, 16, 18, 20 and encourage your child to look at what has been written as they chant through it aloud. This requires the use of several senses and will help commit the number pattern to memory. Your child will see the numbers, speak them and hear the numbers they have spoken.

5   Introduce the following vocabulary as you help your child to solve problems:
3 **lots of** 5,
3 **times** 5,
3 **multiplied by** 5 and
3 **x** 5
For example: Have 5 pairs of shoes laid out and ask:
How many shoes are there here?
Say: *That means we need to find 5 lots of 2.*

Labelled number lines

Once children have become confident finding the total number of items in a set of groups by counting, they move on to calculating using a number line.

They still count in groups of 2, 5 or 10 but now record their jumps using a labelled number line.

Let's consider the problem:

There are 5 pairs of socks on a washing line. How many socks are there altogether?

We begin with a pre-prepared number line labelled 0 to 20. Starting at zero we hop along in steps of 2. We need to hop 5 times to represent the 5 pairs of socks.

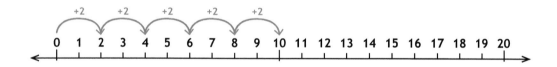

After 5 hops we land on the number 10, so the answer to the problem is:

There are 10 socks altogether.

This calculation could also be solved using a beadstring. Begin with all the beads at at one end of the string. Slide the beads along the string in sets of 2 until five sets have been moved. Count the total number of beads moved in 2s: 2, 4, 6, 8, 10.

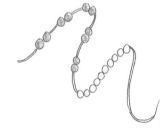

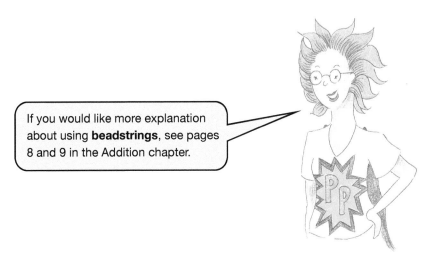

If you would like more explanation about **beadstrings**, see pages 8 and 9 in the Addition chapter.

Children begin practising this method in steps they are familiar with, that is steps of 2, 5 and 10, but those children who acquire this skill quite quickly will then be encouraged to move onto steps of 3, 4 and 8.

In order to multiply efficiently children need to know their times tables. At this stage it doesn't matter which times tables are known to learn the method as it can be taught using any of them. However, knowing more times tables allows children to solve a larger range of multiplication calculations, so the sooner they are learnt the better.

Empty number lines

Once the size of the numbers in calculations give answers larger than 20, children move onto using empty number lines. However, small numbers are still used initially in order to practise using them.

To use an empty number line draw a horizontal line and put zero at the left end of the line. Draw hops of equal size from zero recording the size of each hop above it and the number reached at the end.

If you would like more explanation about **empty number lines** see page 13 in the Addition chapter.

Let's use an empty number line to solve the problem:

There are 4 tricycles on the school playground.
How many wheels are there altogether?

At this stage the worded problem is likely to be accompanied by pictures of the tricycles so the children can clearly see the sets of 3 wheels on each.

The problem may also be accompanied by the written calculation in the form:

4 lots of 3 is   **4 times 3 is**

4 multiplied by 3 is   or   **4 x 3 =**

To solve the calculation on an empty number line begin at zero and hop forward in 3s. Record the size of the hops above each hop using **+3**. Four hops are needed to solve the calculation and the total that is reached is recorded where each hop lands.

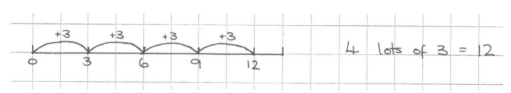

The answer to the problem is:

There are 12 wheels on 4 tricycles.

Using the bar method

Let's now consider the problem:

How many fingers are there on 5 hands?

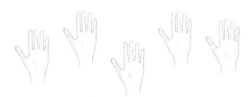

The bar method may be used to help children visualise a problem.

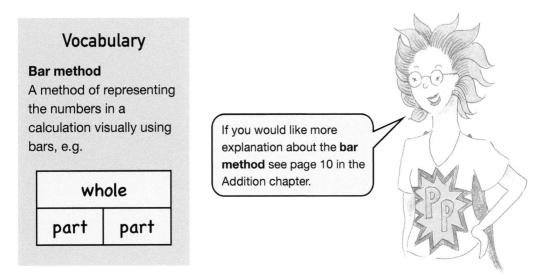

If you would like more explanation about the **bar method** see page 10 in the Addition chapter.

The top bar is the number we are trying to calculate, the 'whole', in other words, how many fingers altogether. The bottom bar will be divided into five **equal** parts to represent the five hands. Each box in the bottom bar will contain the number 5 to represent the 5 fingers on each hand.

So the bar will look like this:

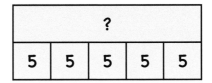

The calculation will be:

5 x 5 =

Using an empty number line the calculation will be solved and recorded as:

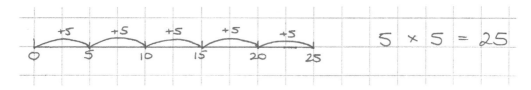

The answer to the problem is:

There are 25 fingers on 5 hands.

The commutative law

Children are shown that multiplication is **commutative**. In other words, it doesn't matter which number is put first in a calculation the answer will always be the same.

$$4 \times 5 = 5 \times 4$$

This can be demonstrated by solving each calculation using empty number lines.

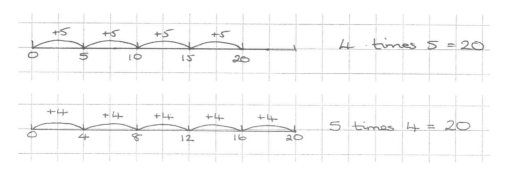

Commutativity can also be explained using an **array**. An array is a series of dots set out as a rectangular grid to represent a multiplication calculation.

3 lots of 5 will be shown as:

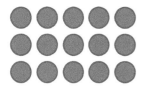 Here there are 3 rows with 5 dots in each row. You can see that the grid forms a rectangle of 15 dots.

5 lots of 3 will be shown as:

 Here there are 5 rows with 3 dots in each row forming a rectangle of 15 dots.

So, **3 x 5 = 5 x 3 = 15**

If we count the dots we can see easily that there are the same number in each grid, alternatively we can turn the grids through ninety degrees to see that they are exactly the same.

Scaling

Children are also introduced to the idea of **scaling** at Stage 2 by making values **twice as big** or **half the size**.

When we make a number twice as big we are **doubling** the number.

Let's consider the problem:

Lucasz has 5 trees in his garden. Filip has double that number in his.

How many trees are in Filip's garden?

To double values, lay out real objects, pictures of objects, counters, blocks or drawn dots to represent the number. Next, add an equal amount of objects underneath. Count up the whole amount by counting all the sets.

Using pictures of trees the problem above is solved as:

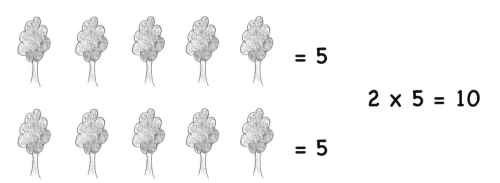

= 5

= 5

2 x 5 = 10

When we make a number **half** the size we are halving the number.

Let's consider the problem:

Lucasz 8 trees in his garden. Filip has half that number in his.
How many trees are in Filip's garden?

To halve begin with the number of items either as real objects, pictures of objects, counters, blocks, or drawn dots and put them into 2 equal groups. Count how many are in **one** of the groups.

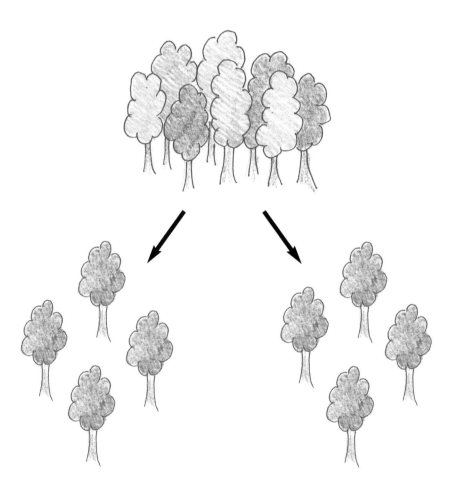

1/2 x 8 = 4

Activities to help at home

1   Count in steps of 2, 5 and 10 as much as possible. Once these are secure begin counting in 3s, 4s and 8s. Solve multiplication calculations by counting through the times table.

For example: *4 x 5 =* can be solved by counting in 5s: *5, 10, 15, 20*

2   Use the vocabulary '**times**', '**lots of**' '**x**' when setting multiplication problems both verbally and written down.

3   There are times when we need to multiply and the words for multiplication do not appear.

For example: *I put 6 pairs of socks in your underwear drawer. How many socks are there?*

Try to think up multiplication problems that don't use the words for multiplication.

4   Use counters/beads/or other small objects to create arrays to show multiplication calculations.

For example: *If we have 6 dining room chairs how many chair legs will there be?*

Show me the calculation using an array.

5   Practise doubling and halving numbers using objects or counters.

Ask questions such as:

*What is **twice** 9?*

*What is **half of** 8?*

***Double** 12.*

***Halve** 10.*

Multiplying using the partitioning method

Mental maths to support Stage 3

Children continue to practise counting in equal steps and learn the 3, 4 and 8 times tables next to support their calculations.

The reason the eights are included in this set of tables is that a connection will be made between knowledge of the 2 times table and finding the 4 and 8 times tables. Once we know the 2 times table we can find the 4s by doubling the 2s, and once we know the 4s we can find the 8s by doubling the 4s.

For example:

7 x 4 = can be found by knowing 7 x 2 = 14 and doubling 14 to get 28.

7 x 8 = can be solved by knowing 7 x 2 = 14, doubling 14 to get 28 then doubling 28 to get 56.

It is important to support your child's learning by both practising the times tables and practising doubling numbers.

Later we will find the 6s by doubling the 3s.

5 x 6 = can be solved by knowing 5 x 3 = 15 and doubling 15 to get 30.

Understanding the **commutative law** can make solving times tables calculations much easier. If we are asked to find 5 x 6 = this is five lots of 6 and we need to add 6 five times, however, most people would find adding 5 six times much easier.

The commutative law allows us to make this swap knowing that we will still get the answer correct.

$$5 \times 6 = 6 \times 5 = 30$$

Vocabulary

Commutative Law
Addition and multiplication are commutative as you can swap the numbers round and get the same answer.

This is not the case for subtraction and division.

2 + 4 = 4 + 2   4 - 2 ≠ 2 - 4
2 x 4 = 4 x 2   4 ÷ 2 ≠ 2 ÷ 4

As we move on from multiplying 2 single digit numbers mentally, as in the case of 5 x 6 =, to multiplying 3 single digit numbers mentally we can use the **associative law** to make calculations easier to work with. This law states that we can multiply numbers in **any order**. If we have the calculation 3 x 4 x 5 = we can multiply the first 2 numbers first then multiply this answer by the last number or we can multiply the last 2 numbers first then multiply this answer by the first number or we can multiply the first and last numbers together first then multiply this answer by the middle number. The associative law allows us to multiply numbers in **any order,** whichever suits us best. This rule will be incredibly valuable when we move onto the written method of calculation at Stage 3.

In preparation for using the partitioning method let's now look at how to mentally multiply multiples of 10 (e.g. 20, 30, 50, 80) by single digit numbers.

Let's consider:

$$30 \times 6 =$$

First split the multiple of ten, 30, into 10 x 3.

We can now write the calculation as:

$$10 \times 3 \times 6 =$$

Next use the associative law to rearrange the numbers putting the **trickiest** numbers to multiply **first**.

$$3 \times 6 \times 10 =$$

Solve by multiplying along the line from left to right.

$$3 \times 6 = 18 \times 10 = 180$$

Children will at some point come to realise that if they simply remove the zero from the multiple of 10, multiply the digits that are left then put the zero back on they will get the same answer. For example:

$$50 \times 4 = 5⓪ \times 4 = 20⓪$$

This is a quick method to solve multiplying multiples of 10, but should be one that each child comes to discover for themselves.

Another law that helps us multiply a larger number more easily is the **distributive law**. It allows a number to be split into a sum of its parts so that each part can be multiplied separately.

Here are two examples where this has been used:

$$6 \times 4 = (2 \times 4) + (4 \times 4) = 8 + 16 = 24$$

The number 6 has been split into 2 + 4 and each number multiplied by the number 4. The two answers are then added back together.

$$42 \times 5 = (40 \times 5) + (2 \times 5) = 200 + 10 = 210$$

The number 42 has been split into 40 + 2 and each number multiplied by the number 5. The two answers are then added back together.

Th distributive law allows children to break down a number into more manageable parts so that they can work with it more easily.

Written methods of calculation

As we begin to work with larger numbers, jumping in single steps of equal size on a number line would require a very long line and would take a long time to complete, so we need a different method.

Let's consider this repeated addition problem :

If a teacher gives each child in her class 3 pencils over a term and there are 28 children in her class, how many pencils will she give out?

Showing this information as a bar method gives:

Number of children	?		
	28	28	28
	1	2	3

The calculation is:

28 x 3 =

We can use the **distributive law** to help solve this. First, **partition** the 2 digit number (28) into tens and ones (20 + 8). Next, multiply each part by 3. Finally, add these two answers back together again.

The method is recorded as follows:

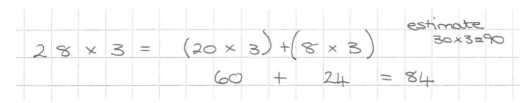

The answer is:

The teacher will give out 84 pencils over the term.

It is important that enough time is spent on practising the mental skills mentioned earlier in this Stage before children begin working on this **partitioning method**.

Now let's solve a scaling problem using the partitioning method:

It takes Hattie 26 minutes to walk around the school grounds. If Alessio takes 4 times as long as Hattie how long will it take Alessio to walk around the school grounds?

Showing this information as a bar method gives:

?			
26	26	26	26

The calculation is:

26 x 4 =

Solving by **partitioning** this gives:

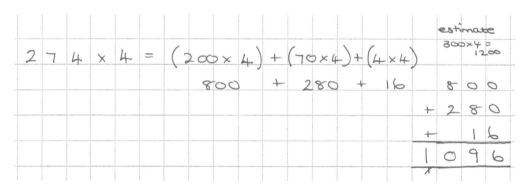

$$26 \times 4 = (20 \times 4) + (6 \times 4)$$
$$80 + 24 = 104$$

estimate
$$30 \times 4 = 120$$

The answer is:

> **It will take Alessio 104 minutes to walk around the school grounds.**

We can use this method with even larger numbers too.

What is 4 lots of 274?

The method is recorded as follows:

$$274 \times 4 = (200 \times 4) + (70 \times 4) + (4 \times 4)$$
$$800 + 280 + 16$$

estimate
$$300 \times 4 = 1200$$

```
    8 0 0
+   2 8 0
+     1 6
  1 0 9 6
```

We first partition the 3-digit number into hundreds, tens and ones, 274 becomes 200 + 70 + 4. Next multiply each part by 4 using the mental strategy of multiplying multiples of 10. Finally, because there are 3 larger numbers to add, we may want to use a written method to add them together. Here I have chosen the column method.

(You might use a different addition method than the one shown above but that will depend on your current preferred method.)

The answer is:

> **4 lots of 24 = 1,096**

Activities to help at home

1   Practise the 3, 4 and 8 times tables with your child.

One approach for learning a times table is:

First write out the first ten multiples. For example: *3, 6, 9, 12, 15, 18, 21, 24, 27, 30*

Try chanting the table through in order several times every day.

Move onto chanting the table by alternating numbers with your child: they say 3, you say 6 and so on.

Put each number on a separate card. Place the cards face up in an line in order. Ask your child to turn over the cards they think they already know so they can't see the number any more and chant through again. Continue a couple of times a day until all cards can be turned over.

2   Find the answers to 4 times table questions by doubling the 2 times table answers. Find the answers to 8 times table questions by doubling and doubling again. For example:

   5 x 2 = 10   *5 x 4 = 5 x 2 x 2 = 20*   *5 x 8 = 5 x 2 x 2 x 2 = 40*

3   Move onto the 6, 7 and 9 times tables once 3, 4, 8 have been learnt.

4   Practise multiplying 3 single digit numbers by leaving the easiest number to multiply by until last. For example:

   4 x 2 x 6 =   *4 x 6 = 24*   *24 x 2 = 48*

5   Practise multiplying multiples of 10 by 2, 3, 4, 5 or 8 by using ? x ? x 10. For example:

   40 x 7 =   *4 x 7 x 10 =*   *28 x 10 = 280*

6   Practise multiplying trickier numbers by breaking the initial number down into smaller parts. For example:

   What is 34 lots of 3?   *34 x 3 = (30 x 3) + (4 x 3) =*

Of all the multiplication stages, parents often find the grid method the most difficult to comprehend because it looks complicated and is laborious to calculate. The grid method provides the link between the partitioning method, where children can clearly see how the numbers are made up and each part is multiplied separately before being put back together again, and the column method, where it is trickier to remember whether you have multiplied every part of the number. The grid method is taught before the column method because the grid method makes it impossible to miss out parts of the calculation.

The grid method uses partitioning but sets out the working in a different way.

Let's solve the following problem using the grid method:

How much does it cost to buy 52 tickets if they are priced £8 each?

Showing this information as a bar method gives:

?							
52	52	52	52	52	52	52	52

And the calculation is:

52 x 8 =

To create the grid draw 2 boxes extending the lines up and to the left as shown here. A multiply symbol, x, is placed in the top left corner to show that we are going to multiply the numbers along the top row by the numbers down the left hand side.

Next partition the number 52 into 50 + 2
and place the parts in the boxes along the
top of the grid.

Vocabulary

Multiplier
The number we are multiplying by.
e.g. 234 x **6** =

Here the digit 6 is the multiplier.

Then put the **multiplier,** the number you are
multiplying by, in this case 8, in the box down the
lefthand side.

×	50	2
8		

Complete the small multiplication grid by filling in
the boxes: 50 x 8 = 400   2 x 8 = 16

×	50	2
8	400	16

Finally add the numbers in the completed grid
together using an appropriate addition method.

```
    4 0 0
+     1 6
    4 1 6
```

The answer to the problem is:

It costs £416 to buy 52 tickets.

If we compare the partitioning method with the grid method for this calculation
side by side you will see the same numbers appearing in each method. It is only
the layout of the method that has changed.

Partitioning Method

$$52 \times 8 = (50 \times 8) + (2 \times 8)$$
$$400 + 16 = 416$$

Grid Method

×	50	2
8	400	16

```
  400
+  16
  416
```

The reason we move our working out onto a grid is that as the numbers get larger it makes them easier to deal with.

Let's consider the calculation:

$$429 \times 4 =$$

Don't forget to estimate first! This will alert you to any possible errors in the final calculation. Rounding the large number to the nearest 100 gives us:
    400 x 4 = 1,600
So if your answer is close to this it is likely to be correct.

To use the grid method to solve the calculation, first draw 3 complete boxes side by side this time, one for each digit in the 3-digit number 429. Next, partition 429 into 400 + 20 + 9 and put these numbers in the three boxes along the top of the grid. Then, put the multiplier, 4, down the lefthand side. Now, complete the grid multiplying each number along the top by the multiplier, 4. Finally, add up the numbers in the completed grid using a preferred addition method.

We can also use the grid method to multiply a 2, 3 or 4 digit number by a 2 digit multiplier which we will look at in detail at a later stage.

X	400	20	9
4	1600	80	36

```
  1 6 0 0      estimate
      8 0      400 x 4 = 1600
+     3 6
  1 7 1 6
      ✗
```

Children generally like the grid method because it sets everything out clearly which means they make less mistakes - it is obvious if a box has not been filled in. As a result children are often reluctant to leave this method behind! Care must be taken not to pressure children into moving on from the grid method too soon. It is better they have a secure and accurate way of solving calculations even if it seems a bit cumbersome to others.

1 Practise all times tables up to 12 x 12.

2 Multiply multiples of 10 by multiples of 10.

For example:

40 x 10 =   *40 x 40 =*   *500 x 10 =*   *600 x 20 =*

3 Children often find worded problems difficult because they don't remember all the different words which tell them to multiply. Make sure when you give them problems to solve you use a range of different vocabulary:

For example:

*What is 3 **x** 7?*

***Multiply** 8 by 6.*

*What is 5 **times** 4?*

*What are 24 **groups of** 9?*

*What are 14 **lots of** 12?*

*What is the **product of** 129 and 4?*

Often children find it difficult to remember that the word **product** means multiply. Try to use it in questions you ask.

The product of 3 and 7 is the same as 3 x 7 =

The product of 3, 4 and 5 is the same as 3 x 4 x 5 =

Multiplying using the column method

The column method is a short, efficient method of multiplying numbers that puts each part of the answer directly into the correct place value columns (Th H T O). However, this method can be confusing to begin with so it is introduced via the expanded column method which makes the workings of the column method visible.

Expanded column method

This method provides space for showing working out. It is initially taught alongside the grid method to help children understand how it works.

Let's go back to using smaller numbers whilst we explore this new method.

Each child pays £5 entry to a farm. If 47 children visit the farm how much will the farm make?

By Stage 5 children are likely to know already that the problem is a multiplication problem and do not need to use the bar method to show this, so it is not included here.

The calculation is then:

If you would like more explanation about the **grid method** see Stage 4 on page 94.

$$47 \times 5 =$$

Solved by the grid method this is:

To solve the problem using the expanded column method, first set out the calculation in tens and ones columns with the larger number at the top and the multiplier below.

Next, multiply the 7 ones by the multiplier 5 to get 35 and write this in the tens and ones columns **underneath** the calculation.

$$
\begin{array}{r}
4\ 7 \\
\times \quad 5 \\
\hline
3\ 5\ (5 \times 7) \\
+\ 2\ 0\ 0\ (5 \times 40) \\
\hline
2\ 3\ 5 \\
\end{array}
$$

estimate

$50 \times 5 = 250$

Record 5 x 7 in brackets next to this result so that it can be easily checked later.

Now, multiply the 4 tens by the multiplier 5 to get 200 and write this **underneath** the previous result again in the appropriate columns and record the calculation in brackets next to it.

Use column addition to add the two multiplied results together.

The answer to the problems is:

> The farm will make £235 from the sale of the children's tickets.

Looking at both methods carefully it can be seen that the answers from the boxes in the grid method appear in the expanded column method, but with one number underneath the other instead of beside the other. In the expanded column method there is still a clear explanation of where each number has come from written in brackets next to it. This ensures that all the steps are included and allows us to check for, and so correct, any errors.

To create a similar, more challenging problem, more difficult times tables and larger numbers can be used.

Let's consider the problem:

Each adult pays £6 entry to a farm. If 273 adults visit the farm how much will the farm make?

This problem gives the calculation:

273 x 6 =

Now the numbers are getting larger it is even more important to estimate to check that the final answer seems 'reasonable'. You will need to consider the type of numbers you can solve mentally to help you choose what to use. I'm using the nearest 50 here giving me: 250 x 6 = 1,500.

Let's solve this calculation using both the grid method and expanded column method side by side to compare them.

Grid Method

×	200	70	3
6	1200	420	18

```
  1 2 0 0
    4 2 0
+     1 8
  1 6 3 8
```

Expanded Column Method

```
      2 7 3
  ×       6
      1 8   (6 x 3)
    4 2 0   (6 x 70)
+ 1 2 0 0   (6 x 200)
  1 6 3 8
```

The answer to the problems is:

The farm will make £1,638 from the sale of the adults' tickets.

Short column method

Once the expanded column method has been mastered we move onto the short column method, which may be more familiar to you.

Let's consider the calculation above:

273 x 6 =

To solve this using the short column method, begin by multiplying the digit in the ones column by the multiplier, 3 x 6 = 18. As there is a ten in the answer this is **carried** forward and placed under the tens column as a small digit to be added later. Next move onto multiplying the digit in the tens column by the multiplier, 7 x 6 = 42. Remember to add on the 1 ten carried forward from before so this now gives us 43. Again place any tens in the answer, in this case 4, under the next column to the left to be added later. Continue in this way moving from right to left along the top row.

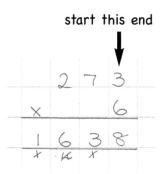

start this end

Vocabulary

Carrying
When using a column method of calculation, and the answer is greater than 10, the tens part of the result is written as a small digit in the next column to the left to be added into that column of digits later.

If you would like more detail about **carrying** take a look at page 33 in the Addition chapter.

You can see that this method does not show each part of the answer separately, and does not convey the fact that a digit in the tens column is worth that number of tens. It also requires us to add in tens from the previous column as we go. It is very difficult to identify and correct errors.

Three common errors are:

1 Not understanding where to record the **carried** tens when the result is larger than 10.

2 Recording the **carried** tens correctly but forgetting to add them later.

3 Accidentally missing out multiplying middle digits in larger numbers.

Up to this stage, numbers are only multiplied by one-digit multipliers while the different methods are being taught.

Times tables

Before leaving this stage, it is worth stressing the importance of knowing the times tables. You may have tried a range of methods to help your child learn the times tables but still they may find them tricky to remember. Children don't need to have memorised them all but do need to be able to work them out relatively quickly. If children have memorised their tables it is an advantage but not everyone is able to do this. It is perfectly alright for them to work them out by counting through the times tables using their fingers. With practise they can get very quick at this.

When teaching a new table, begin by chanting through it. For some of the tables there are songs that fit well with the number patterns as lyrics.

For example the four times table fits well to the chorus of **What becomes of a drunken sailor**. Here are the original lyrics and the ones for the 4 times table:

Hooray and up she rises,
Hooray and up she rises,
Hooray and up she rises,
Ear-ly in the morning

Four eight twe-elve, sixteen,
Twenty, twenty four, twenty eight, thirty two,
Thirty six, forty, forty four, forty eight,
That's my four times table

See if you can make the six times table fit to the tune of **When the saints go marching in**.

When the saints
Go marching in,
When the saints go marching in,
I want to be in that number,
When the saints go marching in.

Six, twelve, eighteen
And twenty four,
Thirty and thirty six,
Forty two and forty eight,
Fifty four and si - ix – ty.

The seven times table can be sung to the tune of **This old man called Michael Finnigan**.

This old man called Michael Finnigan,
He grew whiskers on his chinagin,
The wind came out and blew then in agin,
Poor old Michel Finnigan beginagin.

Seven, fourteen, twenty one-on,
Twenty eight and thirty fi-ive,
Forty two and forty nine,
Fifty six, sixty three and seven-ty.

The eight times table fits with the Christmas favourite **Jingle bells** (almost).

Jingle bells, jingle bells,
Jingle all the way,
Oh what fun it is to ride,
On a one horse open sleigh,

Jingle bells, jingle bells,
Jingle all the way,
Oh what fun it is to ride,
On a one horse open sleigh.

Eight, sixteen, twenty four,
Thir - ir - irty two,
Forty and forty eight,
fifty six and sixty four,

Seventy two, eigh-eighty,
Eigh – eigh - eighty eight,
Ninety six and a hundred and four
and I'm not singing any more.

For the nine times table we can show that the digits for each number always add up to 9.

18: 1 + 8 = 9   27: 2 + 7 = 9   36: 3 + 6 = 9   45: 4 + 5 = 9   and so on

Or look at the pattern in the numbers:

9
18
27
36
45
54
63
72
81
90

We can see that as the tens digit increases by one each time the ones digit decreases by one.

The 9 times table can also be worked out using our fingers. We hold up both hands, palms facing towards us. Put down the finger that corresponds to the number we want to multiply by 9. For example 7 x 9 = requires us to fold down our seventh finger. All the fingers on the left side of the folded down finger represent the tens in the answer and all the fingers on the right side are the ones. There are six fingers on the left of the folded down finger and three on the right so the answer is 63.

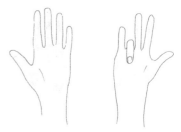

7 x 9 = 63

Practising the times tables using a pack of cards

Once children know the pattern of numbers in a times table in order, they then need to be able to access individual answers quickly. This can be practised using a pack of playing cards with the picture cards removed. Shuffle the pack well and place them face down in a pile. Turn over the top card and multiply the number on the card by the table being learnt. Say the answer aloud.

A few minutes of practise a day at this and your child will begin to memorise the answers without realising. Initially they can count through the tables using their fingers until they can recall the answer from memory. This activity makes use of several of the senses to aid memory, the eyes see the number on the card, the mind works out the related answer which the voice then speaks and the ears hear the number that is spoken. It is amazing how well this method works! When your child can go through the whole pack (40 cards) in one minute you know the times table is learnt.

Try to make sure the times tables are learnt so that your child can efficiently solve written multiplication calculations.

Learn the times tables in the following order:

2, 5, 10, 3, 4, 8, 6, 7, 9, 11, 12

1   Practise the times tables by singing/chanting through them.

2   Practise the 9 times table using the finger method.

3   Write out the numbers of one of the times tables on individual cards. Lay the cards on the table in order face up. Turn some over. Ask: Which numbers are missing? Ask your child to chant through the times table filling in the missing numbers.

4   Practise the different times tables by using playing cards. When your children can rotate through all the cards in 1 minute you know they have learnt that times table.

Multiplying by a two digit multiplier

As children near the end of Key Stage 2 they encounter problems that require them to multiply a number by a 2-digit multiplier.

For example:

If 126 children each bring 25p to school for a school badge, how much money will have been brought to school altogether for badges?

This gives the calculation:

126 x 25 =

To solve problems with 2-digit multipliers children are often encouraged to revert to using the grid method initially to make it obvious what is happening. This requires an extra line of boxes on the grid. It can clearly be seen how each digit in the large number must be multiplied by each number in the multiplier, so that all the boxes in the grid are filled.

Vocabulary

Multiplier
The number we are multiplying by. e.g. 234 x **6** =

Here the digit 6 is the multiplier.

Here the number 126 has been partitioned to give us 100 + 20 + 6 which we put along the top row and the multiplier 25 is partitioned into 20 + 5 which we put down the lefthand side of the grid. The answer to each calculation is then placed in the relevant box and these answers are added together using a preferred addition method.

x	100	20	6
20	2000	400	120
5	500	100	30

```
  2 0 0 0
    4 0 0
    1 2 0
    5 0 0
    1 0 0
  +   3 0
  3 1 5 0
```

Once the grid method has been well practised and the children are secure in understanding that you need to multiply each digit in the top number by each digit in the multiplier they then move onto using the **short column method**.

Using this method it can be difficult to know where to start in the calculation. One solution is first to cover up the tens digit in the multiplier and simply multiply by the digit in the ones column. This makes the calculation method exactly the same as in Stage 5 initially. Another alternative is to draw a box around the digit in the ones column, (in the example here this is the digit 5) then multiply each digit of the top number by this digit moving along the row from right to left. The answer is written on the first row below the calculation. Any tens that need to be carried forward to the next column are now recorded above the line of the answer in small digits.

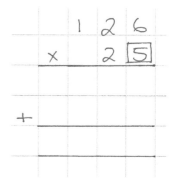

The next step is to multiply the top number by the tens digit of the multiplier. Begin by putting a place holder (0) in the ones column so that you can multiply by the digit in the tens column and the answer will be worth ten lots of that amount. Next multiply the top number by the tens digit of the multiplier working from right to left as before. If you are using the covering up method, cover up the ones digit so you remember which digit you are multiplying by. If you drew a box round the ones digit of the multiplier before now put a circle around the tens digit and multiply the top number by the digit in the circle. Any carried forward tens are recorded as small digits below the line of the answer.

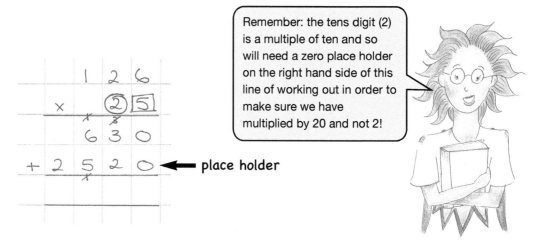

Remember: the tens digit (2) is a multiple of ten and so will need a zero place holder on the right hand side of this line of working out in order to make sure we have multiplied by 20 and not 2!

place holder

Finally, add the 2 rows of working out together using column addition

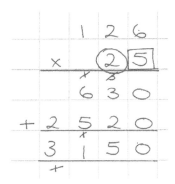

The answer is:

£31.50 will have been brought to school for badges.

Appropriate units need to be used to give answers. So we write 3,150p as £31.50.

From the explanation above it is apparent that the short column method is quite complicated. It requires a good understanding of the processes involved to avoid mistakes. The short column method is quicker to use than the grid method, but understandably, given its complexity, children may be reluctant to use it! It is important therefore not to push children to use the short column method before they feel comfortable with it.

1   Pose problems using a variety of multiplication vocabulary.

For example: **x, multiply, lots of, groups of, multiply by, times, product**

2   Also ask worded problems that do not use this vocabulary.

Ask **money** problems.

For example: *If I buy 6 books for £15 each, how much will it cost?*

Ask **measures** problems.

For example: *If my recipe uses 250 g of flour to make 8 cookie, how much flour do I need to make 24? 48? 64?*

Ask **time** problems.

For example: *If it takes me 35 minutes to walk to school and 35 minutes back, how long will I have spent walking to and from school over a 5 day school week?*

3   Include some multi-step problems.

For example: *How much turf would I need to cover a field that is 17 m wide and 12 m long which has a 4 m by 6 m pond in it?*

(This requires multiplication to find the area of the pond and of the field, then subtraction of the area of the pond from the area of the field.)

If I buy 6 packs of stickers for 75p each, how much change will I get from £10?

(This requires the amount spent to be worked out using multiplication, then conversion from pence to pounds, then subtraction to find the change from £10).

Multiplying decimal numbers

Initially, to multiply decimal numbers it is useful to revert to using the grid method because this method makes the workings of the calculation much more obvious and will ensure the decimal point ends up in the correct place in the answer. To use the grid method successfully children need to be able to mentally multiply tenths or hundreths confidently. For example:

$$5 \times 0.3 = \qquad 7 \times 0.04 = \qquad 0.3 \times 0.6 =$$

One way to approach the above calculations is to remove the **decimal points**, perform the multiplication using the resulting whole numbers then put the decimal point back in the answer.

Vocabulary

Decimal places
The columns behind the decimal point in a number.

Ones	Tenths	Hundredths	Thousandths
3	4	5	5

To get the decimal point in the correct place in the answer the rule is:

However many decimal places there are in the calculation altogether, that's how many there will be in the answer.

Let's solve the calculations one at a time:

$$5 \times 0.3 =$$

The calculation contains one decimal place (in 0.3). To solve this we remove the decimal point and so multiply 5 by 3 to get 15. We then put one decimal place back in the answer. So, **$5 \times 0.3 = 1.5$**

$$7 \times 0.04 =$$

The calculation contains two decimal places (in 0.04). To solve this we remove the decimal point and so multiply 7 by 4 to get 28. We then put two decimal places back in the answer. So, **$7 \times 0.04 = 0.28$**

0.3 x 0.6 =

The calculation contains two decimal places altogether (one in 0.3 and one in 0.6). To solve this we remove the decimal points in both numbers and multiply 3 by 6 to get 18. We then put two decimal places back in the answer.
So, **0.3 x 0.6 = 0.18**

Let's consider the problem:

My garden is 9 m long. If fence panels come in lengths of 147.3 cm, will I be able to put a fence down the whole side using 6 panels?

It may help to go back to using the grid method to solve the problem to begin with. First, partition the number 147.3 into hundreds, tens, ones and tenths and put these along the top of the grid. Then, place the multiplier, 6, down the left hand side. Next, multiply each of the parts by 6 recording the answers in the boxes of the grid. Finally, add the contents of the boxes using a column addition method.

Vocabulary

Partitioning
The splitting up of a number into its base 10 parts

24.6 = 2 tens + 4 ones + 6 tenths
24.6 = 20 + 4 + 0.6

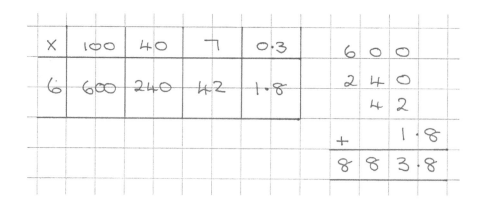

A very common error when adding up a mixture of whole number and decimal numbers is to confuse the columns that the numbers must be put in. If we remember that any whole number would be followed by a decimal point on the **place value** board it helps to line up the numbers correctly.

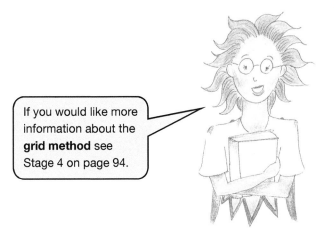

If you would like more information about the **grid method** see Stage 4 on page 94.

Once the grid method is secure children move onto using the **short column method**.

This gives us:

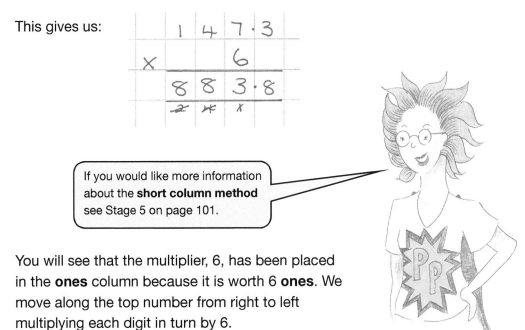

If you would like more information about the **short column method** see Stage 5 on page 101.

You will see that the multiplier, 6, has been placed in the **ones** column because it is worth 6 **ones**. We move along the top number from right to left multiplying each digit in turn by 6.

As the total of 6 fence panels only measures 883.8 cm, the answer to the problem is:

No, there will not be enough fencing in 6 panels to fence one side of the garden.

You may notice that in the previous example the decimal point in the answer was in line with the decimal point in the calculation. This is because if we multiply a number with one decimal place (tenths) by a whole number, the answer will have one decimal place too. However, when we multiply a decimal number by another decimal number the decimal points in the answer will no longer line up in the column and we will need to use our method differently.

Let's consider the calculation:

2.7 x 3.6 =

If we simply line up the decimal point in the columns we get:

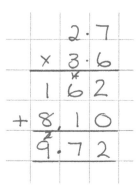

A good way to ensure that we have put the decimal point in the correct place in the answer is by estimating the answer by rounding each of the numbers we are multiplying to the nearest whole number before multiplying mentally. For our example this gives us 3 x 4 = 12. Now an estimate of 12 is a long way from the answer above of 97.2! So, our calculation is incorrect.

Remember we have the rule:
However many decimal places there are in the calculation altogether, that's how many there will be in the answer.

Let's solve the calculation using the grid method.

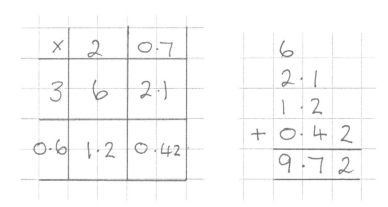

We can see that the digits in the answer here are the same as we had before but the decimal point is now in a different place, changing the size of our answer considerably.

One way of dealing with the decimal points in the column method is to ignore the decimal points completely whilst multiplying out the digits. Then insert the decimal point into the final answer using our rule.

With the calculation 2.7 x 3.6 =   there is one decimal place in the first number and one in the second so there will be two decimal places altogether in the answer.

Using short column method this gives us:

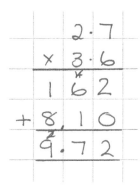

1   Practise multiplying whole numbers by tenths mentally.

   For example: *6 x 0.3 =*   *9 x 0.3 =*

   Worded problem: *A cup holds 0.2 litres. How many litres will 8 cups hold?*

2   Practise multiplying tenths by tenths mentally.

   For example: *0.4 x 0.9 =*   *0.3 x 0.8 =*

   Worded problem: *1 km = approx 0.6 miles. How many miles will 0.5 km be?*

3   Encourage your children to solve everyday problems using their preferred written method.

   For example: *Your Star Wars toy weighs 1.2 kg. How much will 4 weigh?*

   A bucket holds 4.5 litres of water. How many litres would 6 buckets hold?

4   Give your child a multiplication calculation and the answer with the decimal point missing. Ask them to put the decimal point in the correct place.

   For example: *3.42 x 5.3 = 18126*   (18.126)

5   Find opportunities to multiply monetary amounts in pounds.

   For example: *3 friends buy a pizza for £3.75 each. How much do they spend altogether?*

6   Ask how much it will cost to buy several lots of an item that you are thinking of buying when out shopping.

Division

This chapter takes you through seven stages of division that lead to an understanding of **short** and **long** division written methods and will explain why we need to learn both. The difference between sharing equally and grouping is explained. It progresses from the basic physical grouping of objects, through using a number line hopping in equal sized groups, using a **chunking** method on a number line to deal with larger numbers, to the short and long **bus stop** method of division.

When do we need to use division?

We use division to **share a quantity equally** into a given number of groups.

> *If I have 30 sweets and share them equally amongst 5 children, how many sweets will each child get?*

We also use division to **find out how many groups** we can make from a given number of objects.

> *If I have 30 sweets and want to give each child 5 sweets, how many children will get sweets?*

It can be seen in the above examples that the calculation used to solve each problem will be the same (**30 ÷ 5 =**) but the way it is divided will be different. In the first example we are sharing 30 sweets out amongst 5 children, in the second example we are putting the 30 sweets into groups of 5.

We also use division to **find a fraction** of a quantity.

> *If I have 30 sweets and give half to my friend, how many sweets does my friend get?*

Vocabulary

Share equally
To divide a quantity equally amongst a given number of groups.

Grouping
Put a quantity into groups of a given size.

Find a fraction
Divide a quantity equally into parts.

At this stage, real objects, pictures of objects or counters to represent objects are used. Children either physically share out the objects into equally sized groups or place them into a given number of groups dependent on the type of problem posed.

An example of a **sharing equally** problem is where 4 teddies and 12 toy cars are placed on the table and the question is asked:

If I share the cars out equally amongst the teddies, how many toy cars will each teddy get?

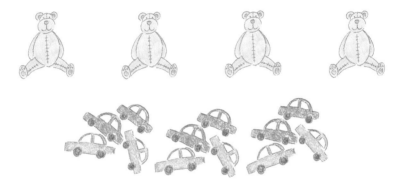

Children are shown how to separate out the teddies and then place one car in front of each teddy in turn until all the cars have been given out. At this point the children are encouraged to check that all the teddies have the same amount of cars and then asked: *How many cars does each teddy have?*

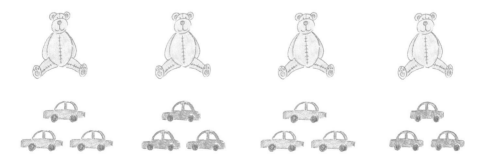

An example of a **grouping** problem has a pile of toy cars placed on the table and the question is asked:

How many groups of 2 cars can you make?

Children are shown how to put the cars into groups of 2 and then count each **set** of 2. The children will then be asked: *How many groups of 2 are there?*

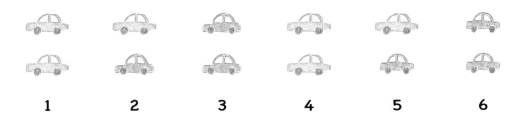

The connection between fractions and division begins at Stage 1. An example of a **fraction** problem is where a pile of cars are on the table and the question is asked:

Can you give me half of the cars?

Children are shown how to put the cars into two equally sized piles and then to count how many cars are in each pile. One of these piles can then be given away.

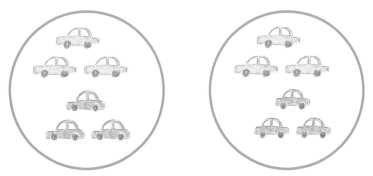

1   Give your child 20 blocks or counters and ask them to put them into groups of 2. Practise counting forward in 2s, touching each group of blocks or counters as they go.

2   Children find counting back much more difficult than counting forward so will benefit from a lot of opportunities to practise. Ask what is 2 less than 20? What is 2 less than that? Continue until you reach zero.

3   As children become more fluent counting back in 2s, use the pairs of blocks or counters and ask them to count back in 2s touching each group as they go.

4   Repeat the above counting forwards and backwards in 5s and 10s.

5   Find opportunities to share things out equally.

    For example, if you are going to share biscuits or sweets between members of the family encourage your child to do this for you. They can physically place the objects into the number of groups required and then count up how many each person gets.

6   Find opportunities to put things into equally sized groups.

    For example, give your children a pile of socks and ask them how many pairs there are.

7   Find opportunities to find half of amounts and shapes.

    For example ask: *Can you cut up this pizza so you get half, where should the cut go?*

    Or ask: *Here is 40p, you keep half and give the other half to your brother. How much have you each got?*

As children begin to record their calculations they use diagrams.

Let's consider the **sharing** problem used at Stage 1:

> *If I share 12 cars out equally amongst 4 teddies, how many toy cars will each teddy get?*

At Stage 1 we shared the cars amongst the teddies. At Stage 2 we also record the result using pictures or diagrams.

One way to record the problem is to begin with a picture of 4 teddies with a box below each teddy. Then draw a car in each box in turn to share out the cars equaly until all the cars have been shared out. The idea of the approach is that of "one for him and one for him" until all 12 cars have been recorded.

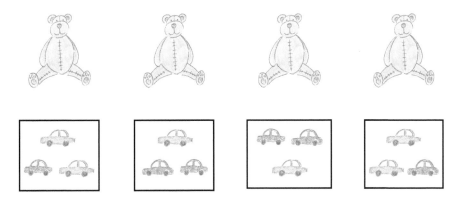

This picture could then be developed into a simpler diagram where the child draws an oval frame to represent each teddy and uses dots to represent the cars. Twelve cars are then counted out equally amongst the 4 groups as before and the number of dots in **one** group is counted. The numerical calculation is recorded at the side.

$$12 \div 4 = 3$$

Now let's consider a **grouping** problem.

How many groups of 2 cars can you make from the cars in front of you?

One way to record this pictorially is to use an **array**. In an array the items are laid out in rows and columns to form a rectangle. In this case the cars are drawn in 2s one under the other and each pair, or row, is counted.

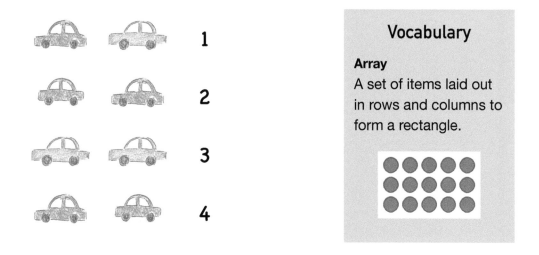

Vocabulary

Array
A set of items laid out in rows and columns to form a rectangle.

The diagram can be simplified by using dots to represent the cars.

The numerical calculation is recorded at the side.

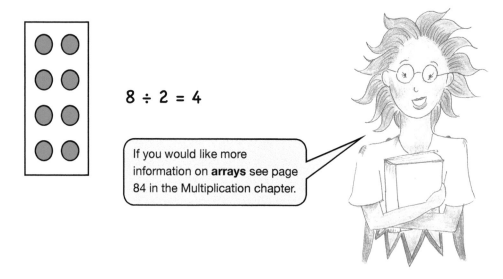

$8 \div 2 = 4$

If you would like more information on **arrays** see page 84 in the Multiplication chapter.

Looking at a **fraction** problem:

Give me half of the cars.

One way to record this as a diagram is to draw two oval frames, one for each group, then share the cars, represented by dots, equally between them. Finally count the number of dots in **one** group. The numerical calculation is recorded at the side.

    1/2 of 8 = 4

Using number lines

Once we start using larger numbers these type of diagrams can become cumbersome. It is easier to use an empty number line. We can show equal sized groups by hopping back in equal sized steps. Let's learn this new method by using small numbers first then apply it to larger numbers.

Consider the problem:

If I share 8 sweets amongst my friends and each person gets 2, how many friends will get sweets?

Begin at the right hand side of the line at the number 8 (the total number of sweets to be shared out) and hop back in equal sized steps of 2 down to zero. It is exactly the same as hopping back to subtract but here we hop back by **the same amount** each time. Finally count up how many hops have been drawn. This method is called **repeated subtraction** because we repeatedly subtract the same amount.

The number line looks like this:

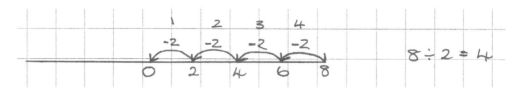

$8 \div 2 = 4$

Using the bar method

Division is explained really well using the bar method. The top bar represents the whole, so in a division calculation this will be the total quantity that is going to be **shared out** or **put in groups**. The bar below is then made up of equal sized boxes to represent the number of groups the quantity is being shared between or grouped into.

Let's look at a **fraction** problem and represent it using the bar method.

Jenny has 35 stickers and gives Blazej 1/5 of them. How many stickers does Jenny give to Blazej?

The problem tells us that Jenny has 35 stickers **in total** and that we need to find one part out of 5 equal sized parts to give to Blazej.

We show this as:

35				
?	?	?	?	?

From the bar method we can see that we need to divide 35 into 5 equal parts so we have the calculation:

$$35 \div 5 =$$

We are looking for the number that goes in each box to make a total of 35. Each time we hop back 5, we share out that hop of 5 between the 5 boxes, putting one in each. However many hops of 5 we can do will give us the number for each box.

Let's solve this using a number line:

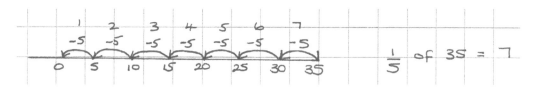

There are 7 hops of -5 to go from 35 to 0. This gives us 7 in each box.

The answer can be checked by putting 7 into each of the boxes in the bar method and adding the boxes together by counting in 7s.

35				
7	7	7	7	7

7, 14, 21, 28, 35

The calculation is:

1/5 of 35 = 7

and the answer is:

Jenny gives Blazej 7 stickers.

If you would like more explanation about the **bar method** see page 10 in the Addition chapter.

1   Give division problems using the following vocabulary: **share equally**,
    divide, **how many groups**.

    For example: ***Share*** *10 sweets **equally** amongst 5 friends.*

    Divide *36 by 4.*

    How many groups *of 4 can be made from 48 children?*

2   Give your children some counters and ask them to show you what the
    answer would be to calculations like $12 \div 3 =$ by grouping the counters into
    rows and columns (an **array**).

3   Give some worded problems for them to solve using an array.

    For example: *If 12 chairs are stacked in 3s, how many stacks would there
    be?*

4   Continue practising counting back in 2s, 5s and 10s. When your child gets
    really good at these, start on the 3s, 4s and 8s.

5   Practise finding 1/2, 1/5, 1/10 of a set of objects, measures or shapes.

    For example: *What is 1/5 of 30 m?*   *What is 1/2 of this shape?*

                  What is 1/10 of these marbles?

    Remember (at this stage) to use numbers that divide exactly. Encourage your
    child to record their working out using dots in oval frames or on an empty
    number line.

In Stage 3 we continue to use arrays and number lines. However, now the quantities to be divided do not necessarily divide exactly by a given divisor.

Vocabulary

Divisor
The number that a given quantity is divided by. It may be the **amount of groups** a quantity is shared between or the **size of groups** being made.

Here is a division problem where the quantity being divided does not divide exactly by the divisor:

25 stickers are shared equally amongst 4 children. How many stickers will each child get?

Using the bar method this gives:

25			
?	?	?	?

From the bar method we can see that we need to work out how many sets of 4 there are in 25 to tell us what number will go in each of the boxes.

The calculation is:

25 ÷ 4 =

Solved using an array this is:

$$25 \div 4 = 6 \, r1$$

The array shows that there are 6 rows of 4 with one sticker left over, because there is one dot (remainder) that does not fit into the rectangle formed by the 6 rows of 4.

Solved using a number line this is:

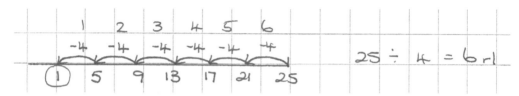

The number line shows that hopping back in 4s from 25 we arrive at the number 1 (and not zero). So there are 6 full jumps with 1 left over.

Both methods give us the answer:

$$25 \div 4 = 6 \text{ r1}$$

At this stage we leave the left over part, the remainder, in this form: **r1**

Inverse

Division is the inverse of multiplication. In multiplication we make up groups of equal size and total them up. In division we find out how many groups of a given size we can make from an initial quantity. So, division **undoes** multiplication and as such is a good way to check if answers are correct.

If we have solved a multiplication problem we can check it by reversing the calculation using division. If we have solved a division problem we can check it by reversing the calculation using multiplication.

Let's consider the problem:

If 4 children have 3 hats each, how many hats will there be altogether?

Using the bar method this gives:

?			
3	3	3	3

The calculation will be:

4 x 3 =

and the answer is:

There will be 12 hats altogether.

We can now check that we multiplied correctly by using the inverse calculation **division**.

We could use either **12 ÷ 4 = 3** to give us the number of hats each child has, or we could use **12 ÷ 3 = 4** to give us the number of children who have the hats.

Using the commutative law and inverse operations to create sets of related calculations

Let's consider the linked numbers:

3, 4 and **12**

Using the commutative law we know that:

if $3 \times 4 = 12$ then $4 \times 3 = 12.$

As divison is the inverse of multiplication, we also know that:

$12 \div 3 = 4$ and $12 \div 4 = 3.$

We have created a linked **family** of calculations:

$3 \times 4 = 12$

$4 \times 3 = 12$

$12 \div 3 = 4$

$12 \div 4 = 3$

<table>
<tr><td colspan="2" align="center">Vocabulary</td></tr>
<tr><td colspan="2">Commutative Law
Addition and multiplication are commutative as you can swap the numbers round and get the same answer.

This is not the case for subtraction and division.</td></tr>
<tr><td>$2 + 4 = 4 + 2$
$2 \times 4 = 4 \times 2$</td><td>$4 - 2 \neq 2 - 4$
$4 \div 2 \neq 2 \div 4$</td></tr>
</table>

Using this knowledge can really help with tricky calculations.

For example:

If we know 14 x 6 = 84 what else do we know?

Using the commutative law and inverse operations we also know that:

$6 \times 14 = 84$ $84 \div 14 = 6$ and $84 \div 6 = 14$

We can find many more related calculations if we understand how to multiply multiples of 10 from Stage 3 Multiplication (on page 89).

Here are a few of them:

$140 \times 6 = 840$	$6 \times 140 = 840$	$840 \div 6 = 140$	$840 \div 140 = 6$
$14 \times 60 = 840$	$60 \times 14 = 840$	$840 \div 60 = 14$	$840 \div 14 = 60$
$1{,}400 \times 6 = 8{,}400$	$6 \times 1{,}400 = 8{,}400$	$8{,}400 \div 6 = 1{,}400$	$8{,}400 \div 1{,}400 = 6$

Missing number problems

Most calculations have the numbers in the calculation on the left hand side of the equals sign and space for the answer on the right hand side of the equals sign. (e.g. $48 \div 6 = \boxed{}$)

A missing number problem has the space for the missing number somewhere else in the calculation. (e.g. $48 \div \boxed{} = 8$ or $\boxed{} \div 6 = 8$)

Missing number problems are often tricky for children because it is not instantly clear what they need to do to solve them.

There are different rules to help solve this type of problem depending on whether the calculation is an addition, subtraction, multiplication or division and where the missing number is in the problem. We will only consider the multiplication and division calculations in this section. Multiplication and division need to be considered together because division can be used to solve multiplication missing number problems and multiplication is sometimes used to help solve division missing number problems.

Trying to decide on the method to solve missing number problems becomes much easier if the bar method is used to represent the problem.

whole	
part	part

Let's consider the multiplication calculation:

$$5 \times \boxed{} = 30$$

Using the bar method this is:

30				
?	?	?	?	?

The bar method diagram shows that we need to divide the whole, 30, into 5 equal sized groups.

The calculation needed is:

$$30 \div 5 =$$

You could use a number line to solve the calculation by hopping back from 30 in steps of 5.

This can now be solved using a preferred mental or written method.

If we have the missing number on the left side of the operator instead, as in:

$\boxed{}$ x 6 = 30

Using the bar method this is:

30					
?	?	?	?	?	?

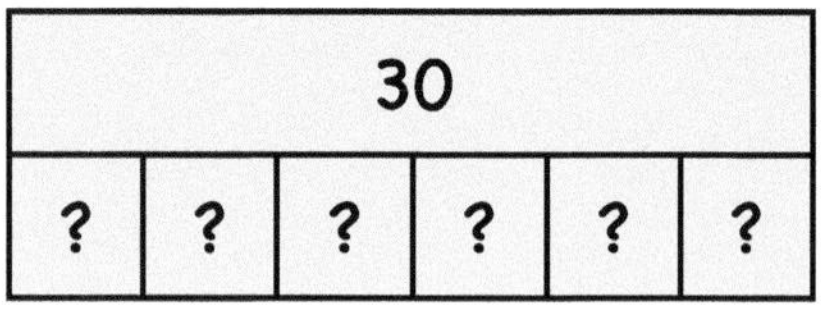

and the calculation is:

30 ÷ 6 =

This can now be solved using a preferred mental or written method.

Let's consider a division calculation with the missing number at the start of the calculation:

$\boxed{}$ ÷ 8 = 7

Using the bar method this is:

?							
7	7	7	7	7	7	7	7

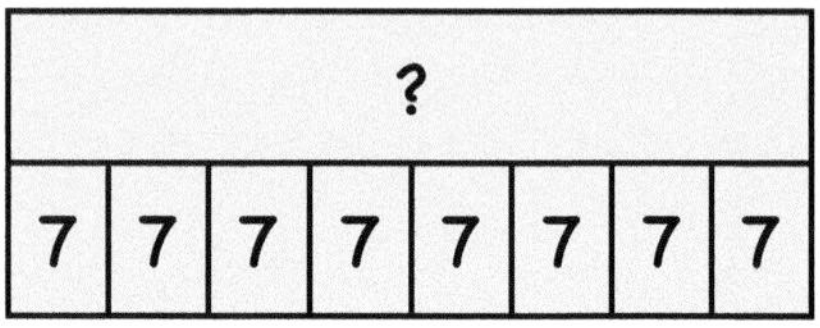

The bar method diagram shows that we need to add the 8 lots of 7 together to make the whole. The calculation is:

8 x 7 =

This can now be solved using a preferred mental or written method.

Now let's look at a division calculation with the missing number on the right of the operator:

45 ÷ $\boxed{}$ = 5

Using the bar method this is:

45				
?	?	?	?	?

This bar method diagram shows that we need to work out how much to put in each equally sized box.

The calculation is:

$$45 \div 5 =$$

This can now be solved using a preferred mental or written method.

> Remember that $45 \div ? = 5$ and $45 \div 5 = ?$ can both be solved using the same bar method diagram, as above. The diagram shows us **either** how many groups of 5 make 45 **or** the amount that is in each of 5 groups to make 45 altogether.

The general rules are:

In a multiplication missing number problem, a division calculation is needed to solve it.

In a division calculation with the first number missing, a multiplication calculation is needed to solve it.

In a division calculation with the second number missing, a division calculation is needed to solve it.

Dealing with the remainders

With a quantity that does not divide exactly into a given number of groups, as with our example where we shared 25 stickers amongst 4 children, we can simply leave our remainder recorded at the end of the answer prefixed with the letter **r**.

The answer is: $25 \div 4 = 6 \; r1$

However, with worded problems that require whole number answers we are forced to deal with the remainder in some way. There are two possible options, we can either round up or round down the answer to the nearest whole number.

Let's consider the problem:

There are 143 children going on a camping trip and 7 children can fit in each tent. How many tents will be needed?

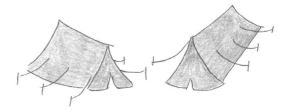

Using the bar method this gives:

143						
?	?	?	?	?	?	?

The calculation is:

$$143 \div 7 =$$

and the answer is: **20 r3**.

Now logically we cannot have part of a tent for the 3 children left over. We must either round up the number of tents needed to include one for these 3 left over children or round down and leave them out in the cold!

Obviously we round up to provide all the children with a tent so the answer is:

8 tents are needed for the children.

Now let's consider the problem:

I put 27 cupcakes into boxes of 4.
How many full boxes will there be?

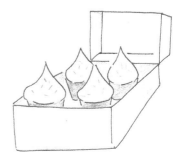

Using the bar method this gives:

27			
?	?	?	?

The calculation is:

27 ÷ 4 =

and the answer is **6 r3**.

The problem asks us how many full boxes there will be so we need to round down (discarding the remainder).

The answer is:

There will be 6 full boxes of cupcakes.

1   Provide multiplication questions that use repeated addition and ask your child to check their answer using repeated subtraction.

   For example: *If 4 members of a family each eat 5 pieces of fruit in one day, how many pieces of fruit are eaten on that day? Check your answer using division.*

2   Provide division questions that use repeated subtraction and ask your child to check their answer using repeated addition.

   For example: *If 10 children can fit in a minibus, how many minibuses are needed to transport 60 children? Check your answer using multiplication.*

3   Find unit fractions (in other words 1/?) using any divisors where your child knows that times table. So, if your child knows the 2, 5, 10 times table find 1/2, 1/5, 1/10 of different quantities, If they know the 3, 4 and 8 times tables too you could also include questions to find 1/3, 1/4, 1/8 of different quantities.

   For example: *If you have 30 counters and 1/5 are blue. How many blue counters are there?*

4   Provide problems where your child will need to round up or down.

   For example: *If tubes of tennis balls come in 3s, how many tubes are needed for 34 children to have a ball each?*

   or: *If 6 eggs fit in an egg box, how many full boxes can be made if there are 32 eggs?*

5   Find families of related calculations.

   For example: *If 3 x 9 = 27 what else do we know? How many related calculations can you find?*

Dividing using the chunking method

As the numbers we want to divide get larger, equal sized hops on a number line become too cumbersome, so we need a more efficient method.

Let's consider the problem:

124 children are going on a school trip and 4 children can fit in each car. How many cars are needed to take all the children on the trip?

Using the bar method this gives:

124			
?	?	?	?

The calculation is:

124 ÷ 4 =

Vocabulary

Chunking
A way of speeding up division by using multiples of a divisor as single hops or **chunks**.

Easy chunks to work with are:

1 lot of	**10 lots of**
5 lots of	**100 lots of**

We could solve this in single hops of **-4** as we did before but it would take a long time and we would need a very long line! So instead we **chunk** some of the hops. Chunking is where we group together a set of hops into one large hop or chunk. The easiest chunk to work with is **10 lots of**. In our calculation we could use **10 x -4 = -40** and hop this chunk in one go. We can then repeat this chunk as many times as necessary until the remaining number is small enough to revert back to using single hops of **-4**, recorded as **1 x -4 = -4**.

The **chunking method** hopping back from 124 to 0 would look like this:

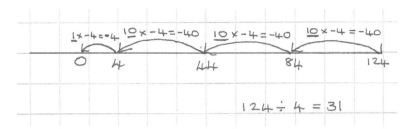

The longer hopping lines are used to show the chunks of **10 x -4 = -40** and the shorter hopping lines show the single hops of **1 x -4 = -4**. The size of the chunk is recorded above each hop. It is useful to underline the size of the chunk, 10x or 1x, so that these can be easily identified later. Finally, the value of all the hops, the underlined numbers, are added together.

In our example this gives us:

$$10 + 10 + 10 + 1 = 31$$

The answer is:

> ### 31 cars are needed to take all the children on the trip.

The number line above shows the method as chunks that are **taken away** from the starting number of 124 working from the right hand end of the line to the left. However, we could solve the calculation by starting at zero on the left hand side of the line and hop **forward** in chunks of 4 until we reach 124 on the right hand side. **Adding on** is often easier than subtracting from. This method will give us the same answer so it doesn't matter which method we choose.

Here is the method of division by **adding on** using the same chunking method:

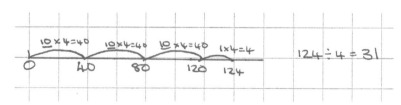

For both of these number line methods the working out above each hop is quite cramped because there is a lot to fit in across the horizontal line. If we use a vertical line instead of a horizontal line there is much more space to record the working out. Not all schools use this method, however, so you may not come across it.

Here is the calculation using the **vertical chunking method**:

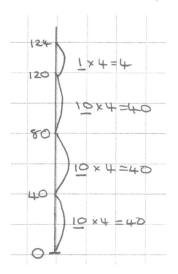

With this method it is much easier to read the working out and see the value of the underlined **chunks**. We read from the bottom of the line up, adding the value of the chunks as we go. Children often like this method because they are adding on from the zero at the bottom, climbing up to their target number.

Initially the chunking method is taught using chunk sizes of 1x, 5x, 10x and 100x because these are easy to work with, but this method can be used with much larger starting numbers and a larger range of **chunk** sizes. When children become more proficient at multiplying by multiples of 10 they can create different sized chunks to suit the numbers in the calculation. It is a good idea to create a data box to contain the chunks at the side of the page before beginning the calculation.

Let's consider the problem:

1,296 people are at a summer camp and are put into teams of 8 for a netball league. How many teams will there be?

Using the bar method this gives:

1296							
?	?	?	?	?	?	?	?

The calculation is:

1296 ÷ 8 =

We now need to work with a 4-digit number and so it is a good idea to create a bank of **chunks** of 8 and put these in a **data box** at the side of the page.

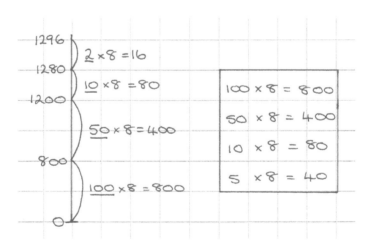

The answer is:

There will be 162 teams in the league.

The key to using the method efficiently is to find appropriate chunks to hop. Knowing the times tables really helps – knowing 2 x 8 = 16 allowed us to do the final part of the method in one hop!

Rounding with larger numbers

We discussed rounding answers in Stage 3 using small numbers and now need to practise applying the same principles to rounding larger numbers.

Let's consider the problem:

If there are153 eggs and an egg box holds 6 eggs how many boxes will be needed for all the eggs?

Using the bar method this gives:

153					
?	?	?	?	?	?

The calculation will be:

$$153 \div 6 =$$

Using the **vertical chunking method** this is:

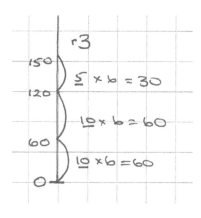

Now this remainder leaves us with a problem. The boxes each hold 6 eggs so we have to put the remaining 3 eggs into a box made for 6. As a result we have to **round up** the number of boxes required to the next whole number, which in this case is 26.

The answer is:

We need 26 boxes.

Let's consider a slightly different problem:

If I have 153 eggs and an egg box holds 6 eggs how many boxes can I fill?

Using the bar method this gives:

153					
?	?	?	?	?	?

This is the same bar as before and so the calculation will still give the result:

153 ÷ 6 = 25 r3

This time the question asked how many **full** boxes we can make so we will need to **round down**. In other words, there will be some eggs left over without a box as there aren't enough to completely fill the final box.

The answer is:

We need 25 boxes.

The general rule is that if you are looking for how many full containers there are you round down but if you need to accommodate everything you round up.

Let's look at some examples and you can decide if we need to round up or down.

1   67 children are going on a school camp. Each tent can house 6 children. How many tents are needed?

2   How many teams of 4 can I make from 74 children?

3   A baker is boxing up cupcakes into 5s. How many boxes can be filled with 152 cupcakes?

4   A minibus can hold 12 people. How many minibuses are needed to take 75 scouts on a trip to the seaside?

5   If there are 9 beads on each necklace, how many necklaces can be made from 365 beads?

6   Apples are packed in boxes of 20. How many boxes are needed for 450 apples?

Answers:

1   12 tents are needed. (round up)

2   18 teams can be made. (round down)

3   30 boxes can be filled. (round down)

4   7 minibuses are needed. (round up)

5   40 necklaces can be made. (round down)

6   23 boxes are needed. (round up)

How did you do?

Remember the rule: If you need to know how many containers can be filled **round down**. If all the items need a container **round up**.

1   Practise multiplying multiples of 10.

For example: *40 x 6 =   1,000 x 3 =   500 x 4 =   30 x 4 =*

2   Ask questions that identify good choices of **chunks**.

For example:

What chunks of 3 would be good to solve:

72 ÷ 3 =   172 ÷ 3 =   2,172 ÷ 3 =

3   Use a range of vocabulary when setting division problems to solve.

Share 62 by 4.

Divide 125 by 5.

How many groups of 6 are in 132?

Share 78 **equally** between 4 people.

Is 132 exactly **divisible by** 4?

4   Pose problems with remainders that need rounding, similar to the questions on the previous pages.

For example: *A school raises £250 for some new football equipment. A set of a football, boots, gloves and shinpads costs £45. How many sets can the school buy?*

Short division is a much more efficient method for solving division calculations. It uses a frame which some people think resembles a bus stop.

Let's begin by solving similar problems to those at Stage 4, but with no remainders, while we get used to this new method.

Consider the problem:

How many weeks are there in 154 days?

Because there are 7 days in a week, using the bar method this gives:

154						
?	?	?	?	?	?	?

The calculation is:

154 ÷ 7 =

To set out the calculation, first draw out the bus stop frame and put the 154 days under it. You will see that the digits are spread out to leave room for any exchanged digits later. Next put the divisor, in this case the digit 7, in front of the bus stop.

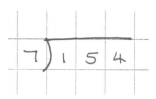

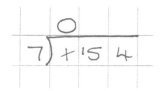

Work along the row of digits from left to right dividing each by the 7 in turn. Begin with the 1 in the hundreds column. This gives us 1 ÷ 7 = . The answer is zero because we cannot make any groups of seven from just 1. We place this zero above the digit 1 so that it sits above the line. This leaves us with the 1 lot of a hundred left over. We exchange the left over 1 hundred for 10 tens and record this by writing a small 1 in front of the 5 tens to give us 15 tens altogether.

Now divide the 15 by 7. There are 2 sevens in fifteen with 1 left over. We write the 2 above the line in the tens column and exchange the 1 ten left over for 10 ones. We record this by writing a small 1 in front of the 4 ones to give us 14 ones altogether.

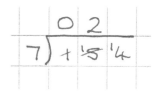

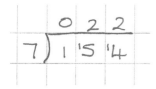

Finally, divide the 14 ones by 7. There are 2 sevens in fourteen. We write the 2 above the line in the ones column.

The answer is:

There are 22 weeks in 154 days.

Any zeroes at the beginning of a number can be ignored unless they follow a decimal point. If the number is less than 1, the decimal point is usually preceded by one zero. For example:

022 = 22   **000.34 = 0.34**

To use the short division method successfully there needs to be a solid understanding of **exchange**.

Vocabulary

Exchange
The transfer of units from one column to the next. Each hundred exchanged is worth 10 tens. Each ten exchanged is worth 10 ones. e.g.
2 hundreds becomes 20 tens
3 tens becomes 30 ones

Let's consider a problem involving a fraction and use short division to solve it:

1/5 of the flowers in a garden are tulips. If there are 130 flowers how many tulips are there?

To find 1/5 of 130 using the bar method this gives:

130				
?	?	?	?	?

The calculation is:

130 ÷ 5 =

Using the short division method this is:

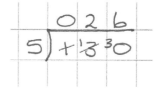

The answer is:

There are 26 tulips in the garden.

What do we do with the remainder?

Once children are confident using the short division method with numbers that divide exactly, they move onto using numbers where this is no longer the case. The issue then is to decide what to do with the amount left over. In Stages 3 and 4 we rounded the answer up or down depending on the wording of the problem. If we want to know how many containers can be filled we round down, but if all the items need a container we round up. However, sometimes we want to keep the remainder so that our answer stays accurate.

Let's look at the problem:

6 friends decide to wash cars to earn some money. Last Saturday they made £267 and divided the money equally between them. How much did each get?

Using the bar method this gives:

267					
?	?	?	?	?	?

The calculation is:

267 ÷ 6 =

Using the short division method this is:

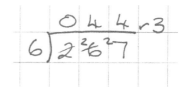

When the final part, 27 ones, is divided by the divisor, 6, it leaves a remainder of 3 which is recorded by a small **r** followed by the digit **3** to the right of the answer.

If we decide to keep the remainder we can present it in one of several ways.

Initially children are taught to show it using a small **r**. So, in the problem above, the answer is **44 r3**.

However, we can also show it as a **fraction**. Our answer would then be: **44 3/6**.

This fraction was found by taking the 3 that are left over and dividing it by the **divisor**, 6. The remainder becomes $3 \div 6 = $ **3/6**

So the answer is:

Vocabulary

Divisor
The number that a given quantity is divided by.
It may be the **amount of groups** a quantity is shared between or the **size of groups** being made.

> **Each child will get £44 r3.**   or
> **Each child will get £44 3/6.**

When working with money this type of remainder does not make much sense. Another way of showing the remainder is as a decimal number.

In the case of money, it makes sense to give the answer to 2 decimal places to show the amount as pence.

Let's look at how to solve the problem above giving the remainder as a decimal number.

Vocabulary

Decimal places
The columns behind the decimal point in a number.

Ones	Tenths	Hundredths	Thousandths
3	4	5	5

6 friends decide to wash cars to earn some money. Last Saturday they made £267 and divided the money equally between them. How much did each get?

We solve the first part of the calculation as before, but once the remainder has been reached add a decimal point at the end of the number and write three zeroes behind it. This then allows us to continue dividing along the row of digits until either we have no more remainders or we want to stop.

Our method looks like this:

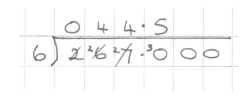

You will see that we only needed one of the zeroes before we had no remainder left so we stopped there.

The answer is:

Each person would get £44.50

> It is important that children understand that we haven't altered the value of our original number by adding the zeroes after the decimal point.
>
> **267 = 267.000**

Questions involving measures, such as length, capacity and volume, also often require decimal answers. The problem may ask us to give the answer to 1, 2 or 3 decimal places.

Let's consider a length problem:

A rope is 127 cm long. It is cut into quarters. How long is each piece?

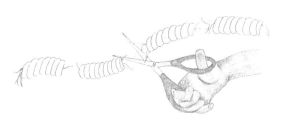

At this stage, children may recognise that this is a division problem straight away, so will not need to use a bar method to represent the worded problem.

The calculation is:

$$127 \div 4 =$$

Using the short division method this is:

$$\frac{0\ 3\ 1 \cdot 7\ 5}{4\ \overline{)\ x\ {}^1\!2\ 7 \cdot {}^3\!\cancel{0}{}^2\!0}}$$

So the answer is:

Each piece of rope is 31.75 cm.

Here the answer stopped at 2 decimal places. However, sometimes we are asked to find an answer where no matter how many zeroes we add there will always be a remainder. Generally, children are asked for up to 2 decimal places in this situation. In this case we work out the answer to three decimal places and use the third decimal place to round the number to the nearest 2 decimal places.

Let's consider the problem:

Find 1/7 of 432. Give your answer to 2 decimal places.

Using the short division method this is:

$$\frac{0\ 6\ 1 \cdot 9\ 1\ 4}{7\ \overline{)\ 4\ {}^4\!3\ {}^1\!2 \cdot {}^5\!0\ {}^1\!0\ {}^3\!0}}$$

For this calculation we could continue adding more and more zeroes, but as the question asked for 2 decimal places we stop at the third decimal digit. We use this third decimal digit to round our answer. If it is 5 or more we **round** the previous digit up, if it is 4 or less we **round** it down. The digit is 4 in the above answer so the number rounds down to 61.71.

The answer is:

1/7 of 432 is 61.71.

Activities to help at home

1 Give answers to calculations and ask your child to change the remainders into fractions or decimals.

For example: *346 ÷ 5 = 69 r1   What is this with a fraction remainder?*

174 ÷ 4 = 43 r2   What is this with a decimal number remainder?

2 Ask your child to divide amounts of money between different numbers of people.

For example: *Share £426 amongst 5 friends. How much will each get? Give your answer in pounds and pence.*

Four friends share the cost of some pizzas. The total cost is £23.60. How much does each pay?

3 Measure different lengths of objects and divide the lengths into halves, thirds, quarters.

For example: *How long is the table? What is half the length of the table?*

How long is the tablecloth? What is one third of this?

4 Look at measurements in a recipe and ask: *If I was halving the amount of each ingredient how much of each would I need?*

5 Repeat for other fractional quantities.

We are now going to look at division using a 2-digit divisor. There are two methods we can use. We can continue to use the short division method or we can use long division. Both methods are taught because many children prefer one over the other. This stage covers the short division method.

Let's consider the problem:

14 children raised £2,354 from a sponsored spell. What is the mean amount raised by each child?

Vocabulary

Mean
The average found by totalling all the values and dividing by the number of values.

The mean of **4, 6, 7, 7** is:
4 + 6 + 7 + 7 = 24
24 ÷ 4 = 6

This gives the calculation:

$$2{,}354 \div 14 =$$

Up to this point, the divisors used have been single digits and therefore the calculations can be performed using times tables that the children know. For example, if the divisor is 6 then we use the 6 times table to work out the division calculation. Children are expected to have reasonably quick recall of all their times tables up to the 12 times table by now.

In order to solve the calculation above we will need to use the 14 times table. If we don't know it, or can't access it quickly, we are best to work it out first and write it at the side of the page.

How to create the 14 times table

Write down the starting number, in this case 14. Then partition the 14 into 10 + 4. Mentally add the ten to get 24 then add the 4 to get 28 and write this down underneath the first number. Then partition the 14 into 10 + 4 again and add the 10 to get 38 and the 4 to get 42. Record this underneath the last number. Continue like this until there are sufficient values to solve the calculation. Children soon realise that they won't necessarily need all the values down to 10 x 14 = so they may stop at 5 x 14 = and begin the short division calculation to see if they need the higher values.

1	4
2	8
4	2
5	6
7	0
8	4
9	8
1	1	2
1	2	6
1	4	0

Having worked out the 14 times table we then set out our **bus stop** frame and work along the number from left to right using the 14 times table we have already written out to help us.

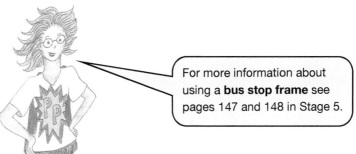

For more information about using a **bus stop frame** see pages 147 and 148 in Stage 5.

Here is the calculation partly completed. The number 2,354 has been set out under the line and the 14 has been placed in front of the bus stop.

$$0\ 1$$
$$14\overline{)2\ ^2 3\ ^9 5\ 4}$$

Moving along the number 2,354 we ask: *How many 14s are in 2?* The answer is zero with 2 left over. We place the zero above the line and exchange the left over 2 thousands for 20 hundreds. There are now 23 hundreds.

We then ask: *How many 14s are in 23?* The answer is 1 with 9 left over. We place the 1 above the line in the hundreds column and exchange the left over 9 hundreds for 90 tens. There are now 95 tens.

We continue to work along the rest of the number in the same way. This gives us:

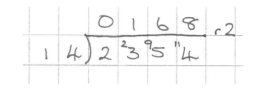

We now need to look back at the question to see if it tells us how the remainder should be presented. If it doesn't tell us then we can choose for ourselves.

The answer is: **168 r2**

Or as a fraction: **168 2/14**

If we simplify the

fraction this gives us: **168 1/7**

Vocabulary

Simplifying a fraction
This is the process of writing a fraction in its simplest form, by dividing the numerator and denominator (the top and bottom numbers) of the fraction by the largest whole number that divides exactly into both, e.g. **2/4**, **5/10** and **25/50** can all be **simplified** to **1/2**.

If we want to give the final answer as a decimal number, which we do with money, we place a decimal point after the number 2,354, add three zeroes and then continue the division method.

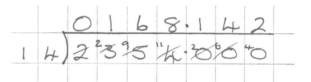

The answer is:

Each child gets £168.14.

For the above calculation we needed to work out the 14 times table first, but there are some 2- and 3-digit times tables that are easy to work out mentally. If you can count reasonably fluently in steps the size of the divisor, you won't need to write out the times table at the side of the page before you begin the short division calculation.

Which of these steps can you count in?

30,   110,   25,   42,   17,   50,   78

1 Practise adding 2- and 3-digit numbers mentally by partitioning one of the numbers and adding it on in parts.

For example: *345 + 251 =*

Partition 251 into 200 + 50 + 1

Begin with 345 and add on the 200 to get 545

Next, add on the 50 to get 595

Finally, add on the 1 to get 596

2 Ask your child to write down different times tables by using partitioning and adding on.

For example: *Write down the 32 times table.*
(Remember, add 30 then add 2).

3 Give a multiplication calculation with an answer and ask your child to check it using division.

For example: *143 x 26 = 3,718.*

Is this correct? If not, what is the correct answer?

4 Set a problem that focuses on the remainder.

For example: *A school has 452 pupils. The headteacher puts them in groups of 16. Will any children not be in a group? If so how many?*

Dividing using long division with 2-digit divisors

Some people find the short division method tricky for calculations that use 2-digit divisors, for example: *342 ÷ 13 =* or *1,654 ÷ 24 =*. Long division is an alternative method that sets all the steps out clearly. It takes longer to complete than short division and uses much more space on the page. However, as it records each part of the calculation on a separate line, it is easier to check the answer is correct.

Let's consider a similar problem that uses the same numbers that we used in the short division section at Stage 6 and solve it using long division:

14 children raised £2,354 from a sponsored walk. What is the mean amount raised by each child?

Vocabulary

Mean
The average found by totalling all the values and dividing by the number of values.

The mean of **4, 6, 7, 7** is:

4 + 6 + 7 + 7 = 24

24 ÷ 4 = 6

Vocabulary

Divisor
The number that a given quantity is divided by. It may be the **number of groups** a quantity is shared between or the **size of groups** being made.

This gives the calculation:

2,354 ÷ 14 =

With the long division method we need to decide if we can easily count in steps of the size of the divisor. In the example above this is counting in 14s. If we don't feel we can do this easily and accurately we need to write out the 14 times table first and record it at the side of the page.

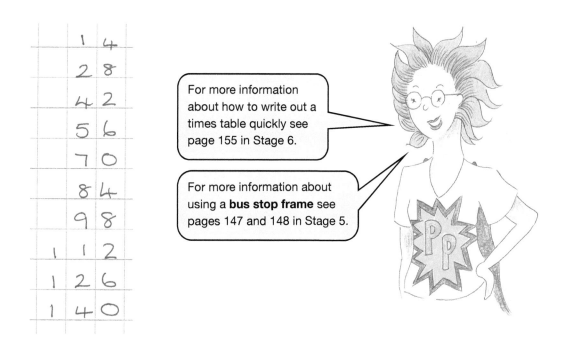

For more information about how to write out a times table quickly see page 155 in Stage 6.

For more information about using a **bus stop frame** see pages 147 and 148 in Stage 5.

To solve the calculation using the long division method, begin by setting out a **bus stop frame**. The number 2,354 is set out under the line and the 14 is placed in front of the **bus stop**.

Moving along the number 2,354 from left to right we start by looking at the first **2 digits** in the number (we do this because we have a 2 digit divisor).

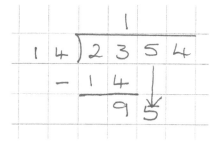

First ask: *How many 14s are in 23?* There is 1 lot of 14. Record the 1 in the hundreds column above the line and write the 14 underneath the 23. Next subtract the 14 from 23 using column subtraction. It is very important to keep everything in the correct column with this method. We can see that the 9 remaining from the subtraction is in the hundreds column.

Next bring down the 5 from the tens column so that there are 2 digits again and ask: *How many 14s are there are in 95?*

From the 14 times table we created earlier we can see that 6 x 14 = 84. There are six 14s in 95. Record 6 above the line of the frame in the tens column and write the 84 under the 95, taking care to line up the digits accurately. Then subtract the 84 from the 95 using column subtraction. There are 11 remaining. Next bring down the 4 from the ones column and ask: *How many 14s are there in 114?*

$$
\begin{array}{r}
1\ 6 \\
1\ 4\ \overline{)\ 2\ 3\ 5\ 4} \\
-\ 1\ 4 \\
\hline
9\ 5 \\
-\ 8\ 4 \\
\hline
1\ 1\ 4
\end{array}
$$

$$
\begin{array}{r}
1\ 6\ 8 \\
1\ 4\ \overline{)\ 2\ 3\ 5\ 4} \\
-\ 1\ 4 \\
\hline
9\ 5 \\
-\ 8\ 4 \\
\hline
1\ 1\ 4 \\
-\ 1\ 1\ 2 \\
\hline
2
\end{array}
$$

Looking back at the 14 times table again we see that 8 x 14 = 112. Record 8 above the line of the frame in the ones column and subtract the 112 from 114. With no more digits to bring down in the original quantity the 2 left over is a remainder. The remainder is either written beside the answer of 168 giving 168 r2 or we can continue using the method to obtain a decimal number answer.

Here is the full method if solving the calculation to give the answer to 2 d.p. (decimal places).

```
          0  1  6  8 . 1  4  2
   1 4 ) 2  3  5  4 . 0  0  0
       -  1  4
             9  5
          -  8  4
                1  1  4
             -  1  1  2
                      2 . 0
                   -  1 . 4
                         6  0
                      -  5  6
                            4  0
                         -  2  8
                               1  2
```

It is obvious why this method is called long division. We couldn't fit many of these calculations on a page! However, it is easy to check quickly for errors since all the steps in the method have been set out clearly.

Compare this method to the short division method and see which you prefer.

For long division it is good to practise the same activities as for short division.

1   Practise adding 2 and 3 digit numbers mentally by partitioning one of the numbers and adding it on in parts.

For example: *345 + 251 =*

Partition 251 into 200 + 50 + 1

Begin with 345 and add on 200 to get 545

Next, add on 50 to get 595

Finally, add on the 1 to get 596

2   Ask your child to write down different times tables by using partitioning and adding on.

For example: *Write down the 32 times table. Remember, add 30 then add 2.*

3   Give a multiplication calculation with an answer and ask your child to check it using division.

For example: *143 x 26 = 3,718.*

Is this correct? If not what is the correct answer?

4   Set a problem that focuses on the remainder.

For example:

There are 371 pupils in a school. The headteacher puts them in groups of 18 for a sports day. Will any children not be in a group? If so how many?

Worded problems

This chapter looks at worded problems in more detail. It progresses from solving single-step, through two-step, up to how to tackle multi-step problems. In other places in this book we have considered worded problems that only use one operation; either addition, subtraction, multiplication or division. However, many real-life problems require more than one calculation to solve them. So, for any given problem, we need to be able to work out what calculations need to be done and in what order. This requires a good understanding of how to interpret the vocabulary in the question in order to identify the correct operations to use.

Understanding how to solve worded problems is fundamental in learning how to use arithmetic outside the classroom. After all, that's why we learn it in the first place. We don't learn arithmetic to complete exercises in a school book but to understand and solve problems we encounter in everyday life.

Single-step problems

When practising calculation methods, children are initially given worded problems that can be solved using only one **operation** - these are called single-step problems. Here are some examples of single-step problems, one for each operation.

Vocabulary

Operation
A mathematical process. The four simplest operations are:

Addition   **Subtraction**

Multiplication   **Division**

Addition

Linh walks 1.2 miles on Monday and 2.7 miles on Tuesday. How far did she walk altogether?

Subtraction

Rajesh has 450 g of flour and 250 g of sugar. How much more flour has he got than sugar?

Multiplication

There are 3 guards parading outside Buckingham Palace. There are 5 times as many in the Palace grounds. How many guards are in the grounds?

Division

Faye shares a packet of 25 sweets equally amongst herself and her 4 friends. How many sweets does each person get?

It is important to spend time exploring the vocabulary related to each operation at the time that the methods are being learnt and developed. It means that children can quickly identify the operations required and concentrate on the calculations themselves.

Addition	Subtraction
add	fewer
more	decrease
plus	reduce
and	take away
altogether	difference between
total	subtract
sum	take from
increase	minus
	less than

Multiplication	Division
multiply	divide
product	divided by
lots of	share
groups of	share equally
times	groups of
multiplied by	divisible by

However, worded problems do not always contain the vocabulary that signals which operation to use.

Here are some examples where this is the case.

Additon

There are 17 girls and 14 boys in Class 2B.
How many children are in Class 2B?

Subtraction

There is 350 ml of water in a jug. 225 ml is poured out.
How much water is in the jug now?

Multiplication

How many legs do 8 cows have?

Division

The perimeter of a square is 64 cm.
What is the length of one side of the square?

With these problems, the best way to approach them is to **imagine the scene**. Children are encouraged to imagine the problem being played out. Using pictures or diagrams to represent what is happening is also a great way to help determine which operations to use.

Let's take each of the problems above in turn.

There are 17 girls and 14 boys in Class 2B.
How many children are in Class 2B?

To play out the scene, imagine a group of 17 girls sitting in a classroom.

Next imagine 14 boys sitting in the classroom too.

Finally imagine all the children sitting in the classroom. This shows that we need to add the 2 sets of children together to find out how many children there are.

We can represent the problem using the bar method.

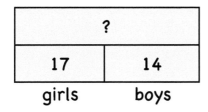

?	
17	14
girls	boys

This shows that we need to **add**.

The calculation is:

$$17 + 14 = 31$$

The answer is:

31 children are in Class 2B.

Now let's consider the second worded problem.

There is 350 ml of water in a jug. 225 ml is poured out.
How much is in the jug now?

Again, **imagine the scene**.

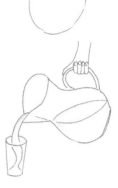

There is a jug that is almost full of water.

Next, some of the water is poured out.

Now there is less water in the jug and therefore you can see that we need to subtract the amount that has been poured away from the original amount.

To represent the problem using a bar method, put the initial amount of water in the jug, 350 ml, in the top bar. Next record the amout of water that is poured away, 225 ml, as the first part of the lower bar and place a question mark (?) in the remaining part, to represent the water that is left in the jug.

350	
225	?

This bar method shows us that we need to **subtract**.

The calculation is:

$$350 - 225 = 125$$

The answer is:

125 ml of water is in the jug now.

Let's consider the third worded problem.

How many legs do 8 cows have altogether?

To imagine this, picture eight cows in a field, each with 4 legs.

Another way to **imagine the problem** is to draw a circle to represent each cow, fill each circle with the number 4 to represent their 4 legs and then count up all the 4s.

Alternatively, we could use the bar method with the lower bar divided into 8 parts to represent each cow with the number of legs, 4, in each part.

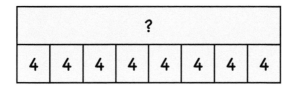

Both diagrams show us that we need to find eight **lots of** four.

The calculation is:

$$8 \times 4 = 32$$

The answer is:

8 cows have 32 legs altogether.

Let's consider the final problem.

The perimeter of a square is 64 cm. What is the length of one side?

We can either **imagine the square** or draw it out.

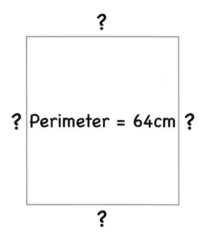

Which gives us:

? + ? + ? + ? = 64

Alternatively, we could use the bar method with the total perimeter in the top bar and the lower bar divided into 4 parts to represent the four sides of the square.

64			
?	?	?	?

From the diagrams we can see that the 64 needs to be shared equally amongst the four sides so we need to **divide**.

The calculation is:

64 ÷ 4 = 16

Two-step problems

Once children are confident tackling single-step problems, they move onto solving two-step problems. To begin with these will only use addition and subtraction.

A typical example is purchasing two items and finding the change from a given amount.

Craig buys a book for £5.99 and a t-shirt for £11.95.
How much change does he get from a £20 note?

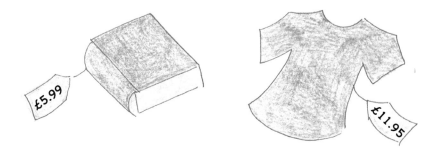

Begin by **imagining the scene**. Craig is in the shop buying the two items – here we need to find the **total** cost. We **add** the two item prices together. Next, we need to find out how much is **left over** from the £20. This is the amount that Craig will be given back as change. We need to **subtract** the total cost of the items from the £20.

Imagining the scene may be enough to work out what operations to use, but if not we can work through the question in steps using the bar method to help us.

Craig buys a book for £5.99 and a t-shirt for £11.95.

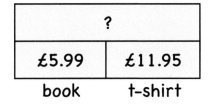

First we **add** the two prices together.

The calculation is:

$$11.95 + 5.99 = 17.94$$

Now let's consider the next part of the problem:

How much change does he get from a £20 note?

£20	
£17.94	?

The total cost of the two items is then subtracted from the £20 note.

The calculation is:

$$20.00 - 17.94 = 2.06$$

The answer is:

Craig gets £2.06 change.

Next, children move onto two-step problems using multiplication and either addition or subtraction.

Here is an example of a multiplication and addition problem:

If a centipede has 45 pairs of legs and a beetle has 6 legs, how many legs is that in total?

If we imagine a centipede with 45 pairs of legs we know that the centipede has 45 legs on each side of its body. That's two lots of 45. To this we will then need to add the 6 legs from the beetle.

We can work through the problem creating a bar method at each step.

First we need to **double** 45 to get the total number of legs on the centipede.

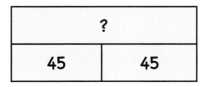

The calculation is:

45 x 2 = 90.

We then need to **add** on the beetle's 6 legs to the centipede's 90 legs.

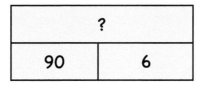

The calculation is:

90 + 6 = 96

The answer is:

There will be 96 legs altogether.

Here is an example of a multiplication and subtraction problem.

Each car leaving a car factory has 4 new tyres on it. The factory has 50 new tyres to put on its cars. If 8 cars leave the factory how many new tyres are left?

Imagine the 8 cars being driven out of the factory, each with 4 tyres. First we need to work out how many tyres have been used. The bar method representation shows 8 boxes, one for each car, with 4 tyres in each box:

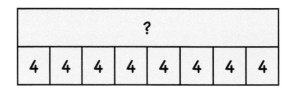

The calculation is:

8 x 4 = 32.

Next we need to find out how many tyres from the original pile of 50 tyres are left.

50	
32	?

The calculation is:

50 − 32 = 18

The answer is:

18 tyres are left.

Finally children look at two-step problems involving division.

Here is an example of a division problem:

A local school has 3 fundraising events. The events raise £176, £81 and £217 each. The money is shared equally among 3 school projects. How much does each project receive?

Using the bar method we can see that we need to **add** the values together first to find out how much has been collected in total.

?		
£176	£81	£217

The calculation is:

176 + 81 + 217 = 474

This total is now to be **shared equally** amongst the three school projects.

£474		
?	?	?

The calculation is:

474 ÷ 3 = 158

The answer is:

Each project will receive £158.

Multi-step problems

Children finally move onto solving problems that may require more than two steps and can contain any of the four operations. These problems are approached in exactly the same way as before - imagine the scene or draw diagrams to help.

> In multi-step problems all of the operations are not always different. Sometimes the same operation is used more than once.

Here is an example of a multi-step problem using just addition and subtraction.

Mei buys a T-shirt for £4.45, a skirt for £8.99 and a pair of shorts. She pays for the items with a £20 note and gets £2.23 change. How much did the shorts cost?

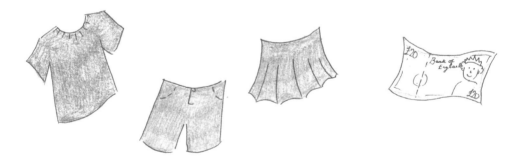

As this problem is a little more complicated let's use the bar method to help us work out what to do. If we **imagine buying the items** in a shop we know that we need to work out the total amount that we spend on the three items.

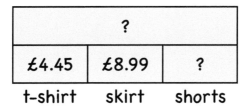

£4.45	£8.99	?
t-shirt	skirt	shorts

We can see from the bar method diagram that there are missing numbers both in the **total** cost box and in the cost of the **shorts** box.

We therefore need to find **the total cost** of the items first (the number in the top bar) in order to then be able to find the cost of the shorts. We know we paid with a £20 note and got £2.23 in change so our next bar method will be:

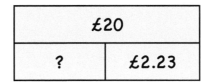

From this bar method we can see that we need to **subtract**.

The calculation is:

20.00 – 2.23 = 17.77

The answer to this part of the problem is:

Mei spends £17.77

We can now put this total value in our original bar method:

£17.77		
£4.45	£8.99	?
t-shirt	skirt	shorts

Next, we need to **add together** the total cost of the t-shirt and shorts.

The calculation will be:

4.45 + 8.99 = 13.44

The answer to this part is:

The t-shirt and skirt cost £13.44.

We now put the t-shirt and skirt cost and the total spent into our original bar method diagram.

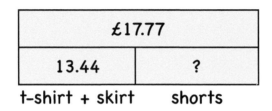

£17.77

| 13.44 | ? |

t-shirt + skirt   shorts

Finally we can see from the bar method that we need to **subtract** the cost of the t-shirt and skirt from the amount spent to find the cost of the shorts.

The calculation will be:

17.77 – 13.44 = 4.33

The answer will be:

The shorts cost £4.33.

We used 3 calculations to solve the above problem: a subtraction, an addition and then another subtraction.

A good way to check the answer would be to use column addition to add the cost of the three items together, along with the £2.23 change, to see if it makes £20.

Here is an example of a multi-step problem using just addition and multiplication:

Charlie ate 3 slices of bread each day in the first week and 5 slices a day in the second week. How many slices of bread did he eat over the two weeks?

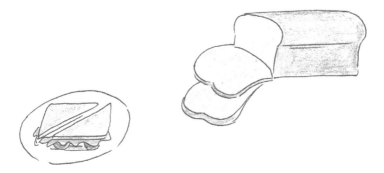

We could solve this using a series of single step bar methods, as in the last example, or use one larger bar method to incorporate all the steps. Let's solve the problem using single-step bar methods first.

We need to work out how many slices of bread Charlie ate in each of the 2 weeks.

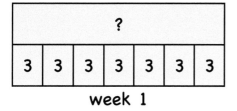 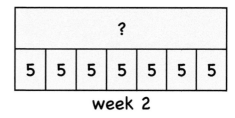

From these bar methods we can see that we need to work out **7 lots of 3** and **7 lots of 5.**

$$7 \times 3 = 21 \qquad 7 \times 5 = 35$$

We are looking for the combined total over the two weeks so a bar method to combine these weekly totals is:

?	
21	35

From the bar method we can see we need to **add** the values together.

The calculation is:

$$21 + 35 = 56$$

The answer is:

Charlie ate 56 slices of bread over the two weeks.

If we wanted to show this problem as one large bar method it would look like this:

?													
?							?						
3	3	3	3	3	3	3	5	5	5	5	5	5	5

This bar method does look more complicated but it shows the total number of slices eaten (the *whole*) in the top bar. The bar below gives the total number of slices eaten on each week. The bottom bar shows the number of slices eaten on each day. If we add up the 7 boxes containing 3 slices, we can then fill in the box above. Similarly, if we add up the 7 boxes containing 5 slices, we can then fill the box above those too. The bar method now looks like this:

?													
21							35						
3	3	3	3	3	3	3	5	5	5	5	5	5	5

Finally, we add the two numbers in the middle bar together to find the total number of slices eaten.

How bar methods are used by children is really a matter of preference, after all they are simply a way to work out what calculations are required.

Finally, let's consider an example of a multi-step problem using addition, multiplication and division:

A teacher has 7 packs of 12 pens and 2 packs of 54 pencils. The teacher shares these out equally into 8 pots. How many items will be in each pot?

Let's **imagine the problem** and work out the steps needed to solve it. We first need to find out how many pens we have and how many pencils we have. Next we need to find out how many writing implements that is altogether. Finally we need to share the implements equally amongst the pots.

Beginning with the first step, 7 packs of 12 pens and 2 packs of 54 pencils is:

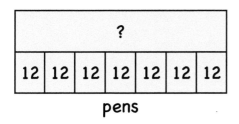

pens

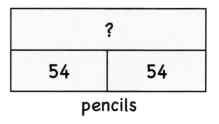

pencils

From these bar methods we can see that we need to **multiply**.

7 x 12 = 84   2 x 54 = 108

Next we need to work out how many writing implements we have altogether.

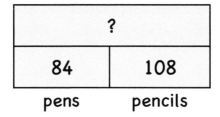

pens   pencils

The calculation is:

84 + 108 = 192

Finally, we share out the implements equally amongst the 8 pots.

192							
?	?	?	?	?	?	?	?

The calculation is:

$$192 \div 8 = 24.$$

The answer is:

Each pot will contain 24 items.

If we draw this problem as one bar method it looks quite complicated:

?	?	?	?	?	?	?	?

?

?	?

12	12	12	12	12	12	12	54	54

To solve it we need to work from the bottom bar up, filling in the missing numbers as we go.

This bar method is quite tricky to draw out and therefore children may prefer to use the series of single-step bar models instead.

Here are some examples of multi-step problems that children might encounter at the end of Key Stage 2.

1   If a bike has 2 wheels and a tricycle has 3 wheels, how many wheels are there on 8 bikes and 12 tricycles?

2   Kwame has some yellow, pink and blue coloured pencil crayons. If he has 7 yellow crayons and there are 3 more pink crayons than yellow crayons, and there are 2 more blue crayons than pink crayons, how many crayons has Kwame got?

3   Maths workbooks come in packs of 24 and English workbooks come in packs of 30. The price of a workbook is £3.50. If a school buys 6 packs of maths workbooks and 5 packs of English workbooks, how much will it cost?

4   Minibuses carry 16 people. A school decides to take 96 Year 5 pupils with their 3 teachers on a visit to the beach. A minibus costs £84 to hire for the day. How much will the total cost of the minibuses come to?

These are some activities that use a mixture of operations.

1   A good way to practice solving multi-step problems is to ask your child to organise a party for a given number of children with a set price per head. They will need to work out how much that will give them to spend in total. Then, given the prices of different foods, they will need to decide which ones to buy and in what quantities.

2   Ask your child to imagine organising a disco and decide what price to charge per head. This will involve working out the total cost of the DJ, hall hire and snacks and then deciding how much to charge each entrant.

3   Ask your child to plan a trip out to a local attraction. They will need to find out total ticket costs and the price of food whilst there. Alternatively, you can provide a fixed budget and ask them how they'd spend the money on the trip.

Maths-speak

Glossary of vocabulary

This is an alphabetical list of explanations of all the mathematical terms used in this book collected together for easy reference.

Array A set of items laid out in rows and columns to form a rectangle, e.g.

Associative law Three or more numbers multiplied together can be multiplied in any order, e.g. **(2 x 4) x 5 = 2 x (4 x 5)**

Bar method A method of representing the numbers in a calculation visually using bars, e.g.

Carrying When using a column method of calculation and the answer is greater than 10 the tens part of the result is written as a small digit in the next column to the left to be added in to that column of digits later.

Chunking A way of speeding up division by using multiples of a divisor as single hops or chunks.
Easy chunks to work with are: **1 lot of, 5 lots of, 10 lots of, 100 lots of**

Commutative law Addition and multiplication are commutative as you can swap the numbers round and get the same answer. This is not the case for subtraction and division.

e.g. **2 + 4 = 4 + 2   4 - 2 ≠ 2 - 4**
      2 x 4 = 4 x 2   4 ÷ 2 ≠ 2 ÷ 4

Compensation Used when adding or subtracting numbers that are close to a multiple of 10 - by rounding the number being added or subtracted to the nearest multiple of 10 and then adjusting the answer by the amount the number was rounded. e.g. **35 + 11 = 35 + 10 + 1**
      35 - 11 = 35 - 10 - 1
      35 + 9 = 35 + 10 - 1
      35 - 9 = 35 - 10 + 1

Count all (aggregation) Adding two or more numbers together.

Count on (augmentation) Adding onto an existing number.

Decimal places The columns behind the decimal point in a number.

e.g.

Ones	Tenths	Hundredths	Thousandths
3	4	5	5

Decomposition The breaking down of a number into its base 10 parts.
e.g. **1 ten = 10 ones   1 hundred = 10 tens   1 thousand = 10 hundreds**

Distributive law A number can be split up into the sum of its parts and each part multiplied separately.
e.g. **23 x 5 = (20 x 5) + (3 x 5)**

Divisor The number that a given quantity is divided by. This may be the amount of groups a quantity is shared between or the size of groups being made.

Estimate To get a rough idea of an answer - by rounding the numbers first to make them easier to calculate and then mentally performing the calculation.

Exchange The transfer of one of the tens for 10 ones or one of the hundreds for 10 tens in order to solve a subtraction calculation.

Find a fraction Divide a quantity equally into parts.

Find the complement Making a group complete.

Find the difference Finding the difference between one number and another.

Grouping Put a quantity into groups of a given size.

Inverse Operations that are the opposite of each other. We can perform one to undo the effect of the other. Addition and subtraction are the inverse of each other. Multiplication and division are the inverse of each other.

Mean The average found by totalling all the values and dividing by the number of values. The mean of **4, 6, 7, 7** is: **4 + 6 + 7 + 7 = 24   24 ÷ 4 = 6**

Multiplier The number we are multiplying by.
e.g. 234 x **6** =   Here the digit 6 is the multiplier.

Number bonds Numbers that add together to make 10.
0 + 10   1 + 9   2 + 8   3 + 7   4 + 6   5 + 5   6 + 4   7 + 3   8 + 2   9 + 1   10 + 0

Operation A mathematical process. The four simplest operations are: addition subtraction, multiplication, division.

Partitioning The splitting up of a number into its base 10 parts.
e.g. **321 = 3 hundreds + 2 tens + 1 one**

Perimeter The distance around the edge of a shape.

Place value headings The letters representing the value of the column the digit is in. e.g.

Th	H	T	O
2	3	4	6

Product An alternative word for multiply.
e.g. The product of 3 and 7 is the same as 3 x 7 =

Remainder The amount that is left over after we have divided a given quantity into as many equal sized groups as possible.

Repeated addition Adding sets of equally sized goups together.

Rounding Changing a number to the nearest multiple of 10, 100, 1,000, 10,000 etc. to help make the number easier to work with when an exact answer isn't needed. The rule is: 5 and higher rounds up, 4 and lower rounds down. It is referred to as the 'high five' rule.

Scale Making a quantity or measurement a number of times bigger or smaller.

Share equally To divide a quantity equally amongst a given number of groups.

Simplifying a fraction This is the process of writing a fraction in its simplest form, by dividing the numerator and denominator (the top and bottom numbers) of the fraction by the largest whole number that divides exactly into both.
e.g. **2/4**, **5/10** and **25/50** can all be simplified to **1/2**.

Take away Taking one number from another.

Worded problem A mathematical problem written out in sentences, rather than as a calculation.

Acknowledgements

I would like to thank my husband, and best friend, Andi, for all his support during this project. His unerring belief that it would get finished, the time he has put into laying out the book in QuarkXPress and checking that my explanations make sense! I would also like to thank my father, Cyril Ford, for persuading me to indertake the project and helping me to identify errors along the way. My thanks to Sarah Wellock for her friendship throughout my career and her fantastic suggestions throughout the progress of the book. I would like to thank Rosie Greatrex for proofreading the final version of the book - it was much needed!

Finally, I would like to say that I am really grateful to have worked as a teacher for 28 years, and laterly as a tutor, to help shape the adults of tomorrow. What an amazing way to spend my working life.